MATHEMATICS FOR THE MAJORITY

MATHEMATICAL EXPERIENCE

Other Books in the Series

✱

MACHINES, MECHANISMS AND MATHEMATICS
ASSIGNMENT SYSTEMS

MATHEMATICAL
EXPERIENCE

§

CHATTO & WINDUS

LONDON

FOR

The Schools Council

1970

Published by
Chatto & Windus (Educational) Ltd.
42 William IV Street
London W.C.2

*

Clarke, Irwin & Co. Ltd.
Toronto

ISBN 0 7010 0457 6

Printed in Great Britain by
Robert MacLehose & Co. Ltd.
The University Press
Glasgow

Contents

Introduction   *page* vii

PART 1   1

Chapter 1   Why? What? How?   3
         2   Mathematics for the Less Gifted Pupils   15

PART 2

Prologue   25

Chapter 3   Mathematics Outside the Classroom   27
         4   Action in the South East   36
         5   Action in the North East   43
         6   Action in the South West   51
         7   Mathematics for Fourth Year Leavers   64
         8   Autobiography of a Mathematics Teacher   68
         9   Removing Subject Boundaries with
                 Fourth Year Leavers   77

Epilogue

Mathematics for the Majority

The Schools Council Project in Secondary School Mathematics (now called *Mathematics for the Majority*) was set up to help teachers construct courses for pupils of average and below-average ability that relate mathematics to their experience and provide them with some insight into the processes that lie behind the use of mathematics as the language of science and as a source of interest in everyday things.

Members of the Project Team (1967–70):

P. J. Floyd (Director)
K. C. Bonnaud
T. M. Murray Rust
E. T. Norris
Mrs J. Stephens
Mrs M. J. Talbot (to 1969)
P. Kaner (Evaluator)

Introduction

This work is in two parts. The first part is written, so to speak, from the boardroom, as distinct from the ivory tower, and therein will be found an expression of philosophy and approach relevant to the learning of mathematics by the pupil of average and below-average ability. The writers, as befits active and interested team managers, have watched many games from the touch line, and it should be remembered that very often the spectator sees more of the game than the player. Part 2 is the contribution of the players themselves; of some of those teachers directly and realistically concerned with the matter in the schools. Part 2, is a selection of case histories illustrating some facets of current lively practice.

Since this is an anthology, you will look in vain for unanimity either of style or of presentation. Each writer has given free rein to his thoughts in his own individual manner. Similarly little restraint was placed on the writers in the choice of their illustrative examples, and as a result there is a wide range of content and a variety of presentation, some of which could be open to critical comment. It might be argued, for example, that some of the assignment cards presented tend to be too closely programmed, and that they leave little for the pupil to do except to read and obey the instructions. As against this, the composer of them might properly argue that at present he finds that his pupils lack the self confidence to deal with more open-ended situations with enjoyment and profit, and that he finds the more prescriptive presentation better suited to his present circumstances. Such dialogues are not developed in this text; they will form part of the content of a later work in the series concerned specifically with assignments. The important point at this stage is to note that matters of detail, however important in themselves, must not be allowed to mask the general approach pictured in the teachers' own descriptions of their work.

This book should be regarded as an important bridge between *Mathematics for the Majority: Working Paper 14* (H.M.S.O. for the Schools Council 1967) and those succeeding volumes which will be much more closely tied to specifically mathematical matters, and their presentation to pupils.

The frontispiece shows us a group engaged on an assignment in the mathematics workshop of their secondary modern school. It serves to remind us that, until we have taken steps to secure the interest and the involvement of the pupils, we shall be beating the air in the teaching of mathematics, or for that matter of anything else.

Finally, our thanks must be expressed publicly to those many teachers, who by talking and by writing have made possible the collection of the case histories. They have, in general, desired to remain anonymous; but the cloak of anonymity in no wise reduces our debt of gratitude for their help.

Philip Floyd
Project Director

Acknowledgements

Thanks are expressed to the following bodies for permission to use the material indicated.

Frontispiece The Institute of Education of Exeter University.

Chapter 2 The Ministry of Overseas Development for this edited version of a paper by the Project Director presented at the Commonwealth Mathematics Conference, Trinidad, 1968.

Chapter 7 The Association of Teachers of Mathematics for this reprint of an article in *Mathematics Teaching*, No. 50, Spring 1965.

Chapter 9 The Department of Education and Science for this part of a paper on Education through Experience first published in *Trends in Education*, No. 7, July 1967.

Part 1
THE SECONDARY SCHOOLS MATHEMATICS PROJECT

WE ARE INVOLVED AND INTERESTED

1

Why? What? How?

A. Introduction; 'apologia pro vita nostra'

In 1963 the 'Newsom Report' was published, under the title of *Half Our Future* and relating to 'the education between the ages of 13 and 16 of pupils of average or less than average ability'. In the year 1965/66 a feasibility study of the implications of this report for the study of mathematics was undertaken by Mr. P. J. Floyd, of Rolle College of Education, Exmouth. His conclusions are embodied in a report which has been published, as Working Paper No. 14, by H.M.S.O. for the Schools Council, and, as a result of this, he has been appointed the organiser of a project to investigate and make recommendations for the learning of mathematics by the range of pupils whose general education was the subject of the Newsom Report. The significance of this project is emphasised by a title chosen for the working paper – *Mathematics for the Majority*; and it may often be convenient to use the connotation 'our pupils' which was adopted by the writers of *Half our Future*.

Half our Future suggested the paramount need for 'our pupils' to appreciate the relevance, both in approach and in content, of their school-work; relevance not only to their futures, although to 'early school leavers' there is an urgent importance in what lies ahead beyond their schooldays, but relevance in the context of the present time to themselves as rapidly developing human beings, with potentialities which they do not always think are sufficiently appreciated by adults and with learning abilities which only too clearly fall short of those of their academically more gifted contemporaries. **Must they play out time until they are released from the burden of schooling? Or can they appreciate, profit by, co-operate in a curriculum, a way of learning, that enlists their interest and justifies itself to them by its relevance?** It is the purpose of this project to correlate any thinking that experimenting pioneers have brought to bear on this problem so far, and thence to seek a basis for such a 'curriculum' which can be developed in to suggestions that might help all those, adult and adolescent, who are actually concerned, at this stage of age and ability, with 'Mathematics for the Majority'.

B. Context and Framework

Our problems cannot be challenged in isolation, for there is at the present moment a ferment in the ways of learning mathematics both at primary and at secondary stages. While much of this ferment concerns more directly ages and abilities different from those of our pupils, some of it (the 'Primary' ferment) involves those who before very long will become our pupils, and some of it at secondary level is already touching the 'mathematics of the majority'. But even what is designed for abler pupils can be a source of inspiration in studying our problems, and our pupils will undoubtedly produce some from among their number who will have a feeling for mathematics and who may follow their abler contemporaries in this, though not in all their work; this is a possibility envisaged and provided for in the planning that underlay the introduction of the Certificate of Secondary Education.

Our project will study the aims, aspirations and achievements of the various mathematics projects at the secondary school stage — the Schools Mathematics Project, the Midlands Mathematical Experiment, experimental schemes in Leicestershire, Shropshire and, certainly not least, in Scotland, and many variants up and down the country which share similar objectives. Briefly these objectives seek to integrate the newer topics of 'modern mathematics' (e.g. the theory of sets, mathematical groups, matrices, topology, etc.), with what might remain (a good deal, it seems) of the traditional school content after much dead wood has been pruned from it: and experiments with such a changed content in a mathematical syllabus bring with them some experimenting with the conventional ways of approach to school learning.

In this country, as in others, the pressure on schools to change the content of their mathematics syllabuses in favour of 'modern' topics has in the first instance come from 'top mathematicians', who are themselves concerned with the increasing demand in the world for high-level mathematics and for the knowledge and services of the small minority of men and women whose intellectual endowments enable them to deal with this. Nevertheless some of the school projects have set out from an early stage to find a relevance in this new subject matter for pupils not of high mathematical ability; this has particularly affected pupils who might lie within the range of a public examination but has in addition been extended, with successful results, to pupils for whom little or no mathematical ability would traditionally be claimed. **Consequently, the development of these projects offers one source of experience that can help us and our pupils towards a solution of our problems.**

Another facet in the framework within which our problems lie is the Certificate of Secondary Education itself. Designed to meet what examination needs might reasonably belong to those in the more able 'half of our future' who were nevertheless not rated of General Certificate of

4

Education calibre, it has in fact not only provided a 'school leaving certificate' for such as these but has also, by its nature of examining, started to exert an influence on the content and on the ways of learning in secondary schools; it is only a start, but even a reading of the various standard examination syllabuses of the regional C.S.E. boards indicates a liberalisation of examining both in content (in mathematics a widening spread of optional topics, including some of 'modern' nature) and in method (graded results, the alternative 'modes' of examination, the introduction of assessment for course work, oral communication between examiner and examinee). All of this, however, would be largely irrelevant to us if the C.S.E. 'philosophy' were confined to the administration and content of examinations; in fact, by stressing as the central tenet of their faith the fact that examinations must follow and reflect the best work over the years in the schools, those responsible for devising and operating this examination (abundantly the practising teachers themselves) invite a learning way of life that is very relevant indeed to us: **a way, of which much will be said later, in which the pupils are actively involved in their own learning, with the teacher being far less of an instructor and far more of an ever-provoking guide, philosopher and friend to his pupils in their learning.**

In the traditional system of secondary education our pupils will normally have had two years of secondary life in the same school before they become strictly speaking 'ours'; unless the age of transfer is changed for all children, this will remain one pattern in the system of the future, although there is already experience of a 'lower school', embracing the ages of 11 to 13, within the framework of an 11 to 18 secondary school. But other patterns are arising, of junior and senior high schools and of 'middle schools' (ages 8 to 12 or 9 to 13), which will cut across the practice of a pupil spending his early 'secondary' years (11 to 13) in the same school as that from which he will eventually be a 'school leaver', whether early or late. With the wide ability range of our pupils, there will be much blurring of frontiers between them and others who are younger but may be mathematically more forward. Consequently the results of experimentation in the 11 to 13 range, whether organisationally as in the function of 'middle schools', or subject-wise, in the work of the Nuffield projects in mathematics and science which include this age-range form yet another facet in our own framework.

These, then, are three contemporary aspects of ferment from the secondary field which impinge on our own thinking — various subject projects, the nature of the C.S.E. and the coming experiments in the 11 to 13 age range (which will be starting simultaneously with our own experiments). **By far the most compulsive ferment on our framework, however, lies in the primary field. All our pupils will, to a greater or lesser extent, have been influenced by primary school development.**

How are we to avoid jettisoning such mathematical benefits as our

5

pupils have enjoyed during their primary school years, and what sort of mathematical learning, in approach and content, will foster in these children similar involvement and co-operation as they grow up to adolescence, in their varying ways and at their varying paces? 'Relevance' is certainly the keyword; and, although our partners specifically concerned with the ages of 11 to 13 take the first strain, the problems presented by children coming from their primary stage with an ability, and a readiness, to think about and to discuss mathematics, at however humble a level, are just as much our problems as theirs.

One common ingredient of the recent ferments is the importance attached to the appreciation of *Pattern* in the nature of mathematics. From the primary stage onwards this can be seen in the pupils' constant search for and recognition of individual patterns . . . in sets of numbers, in geometrical and spatial properties, whether of size, shape or symmetry, in the interpretation of graphical representations. A dynamic definition of mathematics is given on p. 9 of *Mathematics in Primary Schools: Curriculum Bulletin No. 1,* published by H.M.S.O. . . . 'Mathematics is the discovery of relationships and the expression of the relationships in symbolic (or abstract) form'. There is growing evidence of the validity of this in the early, 'Stage A.', development of the children's mathematical learning, particularly perhaps in the way in which young (and by no means exceptionally able) children distinguish between cases of 'no apparent relationships', of 'apparent trends', or of the 'likely existence of a law', in the patterns of their graphs. This leads them on to further investigation and discovery, and in appropriate cases to the use of symbols to crystallize what relationships have appeared. As the pupils mature, this recognition of individual patterns in mathematics extends to those of various definable structures, and to the more precise use of terms such as relationship and function. **The work of the project will, it is hoped, bring to 'our pupils' many opportunities for realising the essential, in-built, orderliness and pattern of mathematics.** Future writings may well offer suggestions which could lead to the pupils becoming more and more involved in the investigation of individual patterns. For many of them an overriding appreciation of the 'pattern' of mathematics is likely to be an unconscious process; abler pupils, and particularly those few who are real mathematicians in the making, will strive to analyse such pattern in the light of component patterns, and will generalise and philosophise from their analysis. This may indeed happen in the case of teachers who, through this new type of approach to mathematics on the part of their pupils, are coming themselves to realise an appreciation of mathematics which they had never been conscious of before. The essential distinction which has been made between an enveloping 'pattern' and its constituent 'patterns' may at first sight seem a quibble; nevertheless it is a distinction which is of real significance, and which could be a determining factor in forming the impression in our pupils' minds that mathematics is more than a collection of processes and pretty patterns, essential though these individually are to its appreciation and development.

C. Do any of the ingredients of these various ferments have a direct application to the needs of our pupils?

(a) Approach

Many people would agree that for all abilities of children, including the minority of very high ability, a 'child-centred approach', involving the pupil in a largely self-operated 'discovery' attack on his problems, i.e. the subjects of his curiosity, is a highly successful, if not the most successful, way of learning. In essence this has always been a basic ingredient of the best, most scholarly sixth-form work — as it is at a university — and there seems no reason why handicaps to its spread below the sixth form should not, with increasing acceleration, be eliminated; these handicaps should not be underrated — they may be organisational, administrative, or just obstinately human! — but here and there pioneers, whether subject-teachers or the heads of schools, are already starting to show how they may be overcome. While such ways and means are being sought on behalf of the abler pupils, the 'examination candidates', they are also being sought — a different, but in some ways an easier, task — on behalf of 'our pupils'. Might it be that any success that can be achieved for our pupils could point a way to even more general solutions, involving also the 'upper' half of our future? If so, it only suggests an added urgency to our project's endeavours.

(b) Subject Matter

Some of the newer forms of syllabus show how irrelevant dead wood is being pruned from the mathematics studies of abler pupils at the same time as new topics and new light on familiar topics are introduced. It is just as urgent for such a mixed operation of pruning and planting to be undertaken on behalf of those who clearly will never reach an advanced intellectual stage. Already C.S.E. syllabuses are pointing a more hopeful way in this respect when they suggest, as topics in which pupils can become involved and indeed fascinated, such applications of mathematics as navigation and surveying, chance and statistics. Increasingly there might be added the mechanics of how everyday things work — could this suggest a blurring of the edges between mathematics and (very elementary) engineering, if not an actual integration of work in the mathematics and technical (handicraft, engineering) departments of a school?

Statistical work based on social or industrial surveys, and involving some elementary thinking on problems of economics, could contribute to the 'civic', and 'commercial' aspects of our pupils' education, as could

7

diagrammatic techniques such as linear programming. A development similar to that in which applied science and applied mathematics are being increasingly seen as complementary aspects of the same things, from primary stages onwards?

(c) Organisation

Primary schools have long ago adopted group organisation within a class for much of their work: increasingly they are adopting it for mathematics, seeing the advantages in it for fostering the values of discussion and oral communication in general, of contributing to diagrammatic recording, of involving the children in making their own analyses of situations and solutions of problems. How does such a class organisation fit into the specialist-teacher, change-of-classroom, organisation of a secondary school? If it is worth continuing as one constituent of the learning situation, how can this be done? This may well be a problem for solution at departmental level, and indeed by the individual teacher involved.

Some problems of organisation involve educational policy, and as such are, in the first instance, the concern of the headmaster or headmistress. Under this heading comes the extent to which subject-boundaries should or could be blurred. The 'integrated day' can easily appear in a primary school, where by and large for any one child only one teacher is involved. The problem is very different in the setting of a secondary school. Yet the values of such integration at secondary level are sometimes shown in the one place where conditions make them easy to attain – in the classes for slow learners in which the pupils are, for most of their work, in the hands of the same teacher. Do the results of subject-integration suggest any advantages for the learning of our pupils? They well may; and experience of such results may well be greatly increased by the trials and errors – and successes – of new ways of organisation – whether of human beings or of buildings or of timetables – necessitated by the bridging opportunities presented by the 'middle schools'. In the meantime our project must concern itself with any organisational experiments that are conducted within the framework of the change from primary to secondary schools at the age of 11; any of these might contain seeds that could produce fruit that is palatable to our pupils.

D. Some questions and implications, for the consideration of our project

(a) The teachers

What is team-teaching, and can it help our problem? Already it is operating in a variety of ways, for example:

(i) The lecture/classroom approach described later in the article

8

'Action in the North East'.

(ii) Classes and their teachers working (usually in small groups) simultaneously in a large space such as an assembly hall, or in adjoining rooms, and mutually helping each other and the pupils.

(iii) A specialist teacher (e.g. the head of department) working in the same classroom and with the same class as one of his colleagues.

(iv) An 'interdisciplinary' project in which subject barriers are broken down and subject teachers work with each other in making their particular contributions to an 'integrated education'.

Will the new organisations of middle schools and of junior/senior high schools bring to light a class of teachers who would wish to be concerned specifically with the pupils in the years in which they move out of childhood into adolescence?

How readily will teachers, on their individual initiative or through organised in-service curriculum study, appreciate the implications for themselves of all the present educational ferment, not only in mathematics? Will this in fact be less difficult at the secondary stage, with its at any rate partially specialist framework, than in the primary schools where the teachers have to be 'masters of all work'? Will this entail of necessity the increasing establishment of teachers' centres, and the complementary spread of a 'centre influence' to any 'collection' of teachers, from the staff of an individual school outwards?

To what extent can teachers profitably use 'ironmongery' as educational partners ... radio and television, machines for calculation, machines for learning and so on? Part of our project's design will be to seek evidence and offer suggestions in this connection.

What need will there be for the teachers handling the mathematics of our pupils to re-orientate their own mathematical thinking – and how can they best be helped in this without scaring or antagonising them?

(b) Accommodation and equipment

Considerable thought is being given to the objectives, use, design, equipping and so on of school accommodation that is purpose-built (or, more frequently, purpose-adapted) for mathematics. The need for our pupils to have a full share of the use of such accommodation and equipment is a special one, and the project will be much concerned with these developments.

(c) Curriculum organisation and timing

Integrated subjects: unconventional timetabling (not only by periods or sessions but even by days, weeks, terms?): unconventional deployment of staff: collaboration between centres of education — schools, colleges of education, colleges of technology — with exchange of pupils, teachers, accommodation ... these suggest ways in which the familiar lines of the curriculum might be varied or supplemented.

(d) Parental attitudes

By the time that the pupils become 'ours', their parents will have undoubtedly been made aware of differences from the ways of learning that they themselves enjoyed or endured in the past. Nevertheless they may well need convincing that changes in approach and content that they have been ready to accept for their younger children remain in the children's best interests as these approach nearer and nearer to the problems of careers and of life in general. That our pupils like and enjoy their mathematics as they enjoy a game will not be a sufficient justification in parents' eyes — too much is at stake. **This makes it all the more urgent and essential that any new developments in the pupils' mathematical curriculum also make sense in the eyes of their parents.**

(e) Requirements of 'after school'

Some of our pupils will be involved in some form of 'further' training or education which will take account of their school mathematics; all of them will be confronted with the choice of some sort of career — even the career of matrimony! **Principals and lecturers in colleges of further education on the one hand, potential employers on the other must be convinced that, inter alia, the school mathematics of their recruits has not only not been a waste of time but has in fact made a positive contribution towards the young adult's worth as a citizen, as an employee, as a further pupil.** The project will make strong attempts to enlist the interest and the active co-operation of such persons as will be responsible for 'handling' the young school leaver.

Why the project? A pulling together of strings

Opportunity is being widely taken at the present moment, largely within the context of problems involved in raising the school leaving age, of discussing ways and means of promoting relevance in — and, just as important, eliminating irrelevance from — the 'education of the majority'. Experiments are being staged and the results of these can be more widely, and more speedily, presented to others in the educational field through ways of communication that have recently and significantly spread; the work of the Schools Council itself is largely directed towards this end, and the influence of 'teachers' centres' has already shown itself as one of the most powerful educational developments. The use of team teaching, of closed-circuit television of the national educational broadcasts, of programmed learning, of teaching machines − all of these new resources are being tried and the results are being publicised, discussed and tried out in new contexts. Is it too much to claim as an embracing objective of this 'new education' the nurturing of succeeding generations of adults who have been accustomed throughout their school learning to thinking for themselves, while developing a fluency and variety of communication with others (whether in words or on paper) that will stand them in good stead later on in work and in leisure? Accepting this objective, our project believes that the 'mathematics of the majority' has a considerable part to play in its achievement.

Some thoughts on the nature of a mathematical education

From the experience of recent developments in the mathematics in primary schools an impression is gained of the potential pervasiveness of mathematics and its way of thinking, although it is increasingly difficult to define exactly where 'mathematics' begins and ends. Certainly this does not trouble the children, who show that the thinking and consequent discussion which are inseparable from this type of working bring them a sense of enjoyment and a deep satisfaction, and this seems to be true alike of the younger and older primary children, of the abler and the less − indeed the least − able. Our project will aim at engendering at its particular level of age and ability, a comparable experience of 'mathematical pervasiveness' in its pupils. **But the more fully that the teachers have taken a fresh look at the nature and implications of mathematics, the richer this experience can be, and the following section is included in order to serve as a guide in this direction.**

Three major characteristics might be discussed in a study of mathematics:

(i) the part it plays in providing language and tools for the expression and solution of scientific and practical problems.

(ii) its essential nature as the 'science of number and space', leading to the discovery of relationships in number and in the ingredients of natural and man-made 'worlds'.

(iii) its possession of a structure of clear, logical argument − a structure that at times may not be related to the 'real world' at all.

11

'Our pupils' will be almost entirely concerned with characteristics (i) and (ii). Nevertheless, if their approach to mathematics has been based on experience and on the encouragement of good attitudes and on ability to think and to make decisions for themselves, they will come increasingly to appreciate that there *are* reasons to account for mathematical phenomena, even though such reasons are beyond their powers to grasp. To some extent this will be implicit in the more conscious structuring of experience, as content and ideas are developed, which will come as the pupils mature through their secondary years.

What might be considered as essential ingredients in the content of a mathematical education? These points might give some guidance.

(i) A spirit of discovery − what could be described as 'working like a scientist'.

(ii) The expectation and recognition of patterns and relationships 'whenever there is mathematics'. So fundamental is this concept that a special section will be devoted later on in this series to expanding and developing it.

(iii) The acquisition of 'knowhow' in utilitarian mathematics, when the subject plays its part as a tool and a servant for assisting the solution of everyday problems.

(iv) Complementary to the standard techniques acquired in (iii) is the need for the pupils to gain some experience, however elementary and humble of having to confront problems that are not of instantly recognisable types, and for which solutions cannot be drawn out of well-familiarised pigeonholes.

(v) Any rigour in proof and deduction is relative to the stage of working. Nevertheless as has been said above, it is important for the pupils to realise that mathematical reasons do exist, even when the search for them is clearly inappropriate. Moreover, even 'our pupils' do welcome suitable 'justifications' to account for mathematical situations, even if the teacher realises that no rigorous proof can be claimed. An example might be the 'discovery' of the formula for the area of a circle by the familiar procedure of dividing the circle into small sections which are then placed alongside each other so as to form a 'near rectangle' with sides 'r' and 'πr' in lengths. The 'deduction' of πr^2 for the area of the circle offers a sort of probable justification to a pupil who could not begin to appreciate the logic of a theory of limits.

Beyond the content-ingredients in a mathematical education there are surely specific qualities that a teacher aims at nurturing. Such qualities could include, in addition to the confidence which can stem from knowledge and from a command of techniques, the readiness to display imagination and to exercise initiative: the readiness to judge a mathematical situation and to decide on ways and means of dealing with it; the persistence needed to carry out what has been decided on: and last, but very far from least, the ability to communicate, whether orally or in writing, or by diagram as seems most appropriate, the process of tackling the mathematical situation, the results obtained and any inferences from the results.

Traditionally the different items of a mathematics syllabus have been carefully listed in the context of when they would be first met with and then covered by the pupil. Nowadays, with the 'Stage A' of topics being increasingly experienced by younger or less able pupils, the written expression of a syllabus is not so simple — it has to reflect a situation in which the pupil repeatedly experiences such topics, as he gets older and more mature. Consequently a syllabus might indicate the mathematical development of the range of pupils for whom it is intended under broad headings, such as:

(a) Topics, with the concepts and skills involved: listed under sub-headings such as number appreciation; shape, size, similarity. Symmetry — spatial relationships in general: probability and statistics: with unifying threads such as proportionality (appearing both in number and in spatial relationships). Among the 'skills' could be included the use of computational aids.

(b) Language: representation and communication of mathematics by words, numbers, symbols; in 'straight writing': by models and diagrams; by various forms of graph: by the use of the language of 'ordinary' algebra: by the use of 'set' language and symbols.

(c) Structured order in number relations, in operations, in the existence (or absence) of 'pervading laws' (commutativity) to such extent as is appropriate to the stage of learning of the pupil; and in the case of 'our pupils', this might be very little although *their* mathematical experience can be enriched if *the teacher* has an appreciation of mathematical 'order'.

Operational

To this end the project organiser has recruited a small full-time staff as his constant partners. Their work will be, in its fullest sense, to devise 'materials' that will help those in the schools. But their own inspiration will be drawn extensively from the work of a large number of collaborators from all parts of the country. Some of these may make specific contributions by writing short monographs on topics with which they are especially familiar. Others will contribute the ideas and results of experiments in their schools, and these will include those working in a network of pilot and associated areas which have agreed to co-operate in the project's work. There will, however, also be included anyone from anywhere who has put thought into action in the interests of the majority's mathematics: to such as him the project extends the urgent invitation not to hide his light under a bushel! In fact the opening up of channels of inter-communication could be not the least important of the project's objects and attainments, for all the partners in education can contribute to its growing symposium of effort and experience — the whole teaching fraternity in school or college, administrators, organisers, inspectors. Perhaps a 'teaching centre influence', in all ways and at all levels, could come into effect to ensure the greatest ease and the widest spread for such inter-communication? On such must the success of our project depend, and with it the hopes it could bring for the 'mathematics of the majority'. Difficulties are formidable and are not to be underrated; our declaration of intent is that we will secure all the help we can in overcoming them, and that we will try to build foundations on which our pupils, the 'half of our future', can think and choose and use mathematically, in their own interests of the adult world into which they are growing up.

2

Mathematics for the Less Gifted Pupils

Some forms of mathematics are patently at the heart of much of the scientific and technological development which is such an ever rapidly changing feature of modern society; indeed, not only is mathematics at the heart, it is also the actual life blood of some of these developments. As a consequence, there has emerged an extensive class of person, unknown in previous centuries outside universities — a class which for its professional uses needs mathematical training, as distinct from instruction in mere arithmetical skill. This class will clearly be drawn from the higher ability pupils. The majority of our pupils will neither need nor demand such an exacting training in mathematics; but at the same time they will have to live, as intelligent citizens, in a society which is becoming more and more influenced by mathematics and technology. The need for a mathematical education which emphasises mathematical literacy rather than the acquisition of a collection of mathematical skills lies at the core of many present projects in mathematical educational development.

Mathematics in some form or other, equally with music, art, drama and literature is part of the cultural heritage of a society; this has been true in past centuries, and it is equally true today. It is the study of mathematics as part of a cultural heritage rather than of mathematics as a utilitarian aid which should occupy the attention of those concerned with the majority of pupils, including also the less gifted pupils.

In short, we should be engaged in the mathematical education of twentieth century citizens rather than in the production of potential professional mathematicians. This is not to deny the importance and urgency of ever increasing the supply of those persons who have professional mathematical training, but it must be stressed that these are not the concern of this paper, which deals with the majority of our pupils, half of whom will remain 'below average', no matter what progress is made in their mathematical education.

The enjoyment and the appreciation of music, whether that of Bach, Beethoven, Britten or the Beatles, are not the sole province of trained musicians: still less are they dependent on musical executive ability. The expertise of the trained musician can lead to deeper enjoyment and more critical appreciation, but, nevertheless, the ordinary citizen gets his own full share of enjoyment and appreciation if he is prepared actively to listen rather than just to hear. In like manner, a degree of enjoyment and appreciation of some mathematics, it may be of Boole or perhaps of the

15

Bernoulli family, need not be altogether dependent on intensive mathematical training and the acquisition of mathematical techniques. As with music, mathematics has something of value and pleasure to offer to any ordinary citizen who is prepared to seek the revelation; for, unlike music, which is heard and so reveals its presence through sound, mathematics rarely reveals even its presence except to the active seeker. The analogy should not be pressed too far, but it was chosen with care as many mathematicians are musicians also, and many musicians evince an interest in mathematics. To list the intersection of these sets would prove lengthy, and one named example must suffice — Albert Einstein. The factors common to these superficially different fields of human activity, music and mathematics, appear to be a keen appreciation of structure and of pattern. Mathematical education could thus so far be regarded as a trident with structure, pattern and revelation as its three prongs.

Before lengthening these three prongs somewhat, let us consider what it may be that can make mathematics relevant to the youngster of today, for it is through his eyes that we must try to view the situation. The abstract, so called 'pure', mathematician of the upper stratum rightly holds mathematics in high regard for what it *is*, and not only for what, with a combination of intellect and technique, he can do with it. The general citizen, of lesser intellectual calibre and lacking specialised techniques, values mathematics largely for what it *does*. Its potential future use to society (even if this proves accurately predictable) is of little import to our general pupil; that he has to learn it 'because it is good for him', is an argument which cuts no ice at all with him. If, then, accomplishment is the touchstone which we are to apply to mathematics and its learning, then it clearly behoves us to create a learning situation in which the accomplishment becomes manifestly achieved by the pupil himself, as well as to those around him. He must succeed, no matter how simple the task, and moreover he must be conscious of his success, no matter how small — small that is by mature and adult standards. The adage that 'nothing succeeds like success' is particularly applicable to our less gifted pupil. It is a taste of success as opposed to a feeling of frustration, failure and guilt, which will place him firmly on a sound mathematical road. Intellectual limitations may reduce the distance he can travel along that road but at least he will be moving, however slowly, in the right direction, and above all he will be enjoying and appreciating his mathematical journey.

In the foregoing discussion, the connotation to be applied to accomplishment has drifted from the field of mathematics itself into the field of pupil achievement. This presents no dichotomy, for in successful mathematical education the two aspects are so inextricably interwoven as to appear inseparable. In reply to the question as to what mathematical accomplishments present a particular appeal to the average pupil, it must be admitted that our present knowledge based on the pupil/classroom situation is slight, but more and more is coming to light as a result not only of the experimental work emerging from some projects (1) but also of the initiative, zeal and imagination of a number of pioneering teachers working in consort with their pupils (2). Such teachers earn our gratitude for their conviction in breaking free from a situation where the work of the less gifted youngsters often is, for the most part, a watered down version of the academic courses followed by abler pupils. The references given at the end of Part I will provide some detail of the action of these workers, but only general comment will be presented here.

On the matter of mathematical content, these writers offer material which is well outside the limited field of arithmetical computation, although that receives its due share of attention. Valid geometrical studies, three dimensional, plane, metrical and topological are either presented or are projected. The language and symbolism of sets is introduced at an early stage and serves to unify later working. The pupil meets, at an appropriate level, algebraic skills. Such themes as a study of number bases other than the denary, of modular arithmetic, of experimental probability, of descriptive statistics variously make their appearance. The list is not exhaustive but it serves to make us pause and think how far, in the past, we have underestimated the mathematical ability of our pupils. It could quite well be that we have confused the ability of a pupil to think and respond mathematically with his computational skill, which in all honesty is often limited. The factor which appears common to these works is that of structure and pattern, involving investigation by the pupil rather than rote learning of prescribed rules. If structure, pattern and revelation are to be regarded as prongs, then pupil achievement must be regarded as the shaft of the trident. The shaft may be a short one or rather longer as the case may be: its length must depend on the ability of the pupil, but of its strength and effectiveness there must be no question at all.

The matter of revelation requires some further consideration. A skilled and knowledgable searcher walking along a suitable pebble beach will soon fill his bag with semi-precious stones — amethyst, moss agates or whatever stones are prevalent on that beach. A less skilled or less knowledgable searcher may merely collect some pretty specimens, and there the matter often rests. On the other hand he may take subsequent steps to identify the pretty pebbles he has found and so go some way towards becoming an expert in semi-precious stones. Like pebble discovery, mathematical discovery depends to a large extent on knowing what you are looking for — that is if you are in the class of the first searcher; in fact you use your previous knowledge and experience as a base for further development. If you are in the class of the second searcher, it is a matter of motivation and contact with suitable sources whether your discovery is merely a dead end or whether it leads to learning developments. It may well be regarded as the prime function of the teacher in the discovery approach to mathematics learning to act as motivator and source, in other words, to be a real teacher as distinct from being a mathematical indoctrinator. Present day experiences suggest that the majority of the less gifted pupils are in the position of the second searcher, and furthermore that they will lean heavily on the supporting arms of their teachers. This is not an argument for depriving the less gifted of the joys and tensions of discovery; rather is it a plea for recognition by the teachers of the nature and degree of support to be provided in any individual case.

From the viewpoint that the nature of the learning experiences undergone by the pupil are of more lasting consequence than the actual mathematical content of his course, a brief contrast between the 'traditional' and 'new' approaches to mathematics teaching will be relevant at this point. The falsity of divorcing approach from content should be apparent to all, but nevertheless some separate consideration is given in the interests of presentation.

The terms 'traditional' and 'new' are used merely to distinguish that to which we have grown accustomed from that with which we are unfamiliar (or much less familiar).

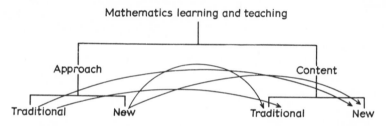

Mathematics learning and teaching

Fig. 1. (An oversimplification which will be used as a 'starter')

Bearing in mind the meanings to be given to the words 'traditional' and 'new', it is necessary to point out that in practice the distinctions are not at all as clear cut as Fig. 1 suggests. The fact that it is possible to treat traditional content with a new approach, or alternatively to treat new content with a traditional approach, should not be overlooked.

Any of the four possibilities emanating from Fig. 1 could provide a strategy for the mathematical work of a school. The short-comings and malfunctioning of the traditional approach with less gifted children are so apparent that it is hoped that the total possible is thereby reduced to two.

J. B. Biggs in *Mathematics and Conditions of Learning* (3) makes a detailed analysis of approaches used in the mathematics teaching and it is on his work that the following thoughts are mainly based.

The Traditional Approach, characterised and simplified

(a) Excessive repetition with similar experiences or data.

(b) Data that are of the same kind as that finally reproduced, i.e. symbols.

18

(c) Extrinsic motivation and irrelevant rewards.

(d) A background of past experiences and general class atmosphere that is likely to produce a set for mechanistic and reproductive classroom strategies.

The school consequences of such a stark pattern are equally stark and rigid.
In brief they amount to:

(i) Streaming into allegedly homogenous groups.

(ii) A preponderance of repetitive mechanical drill mainly involving symbols, and a lack of concrete experiences involving physical material.

(iii) Standard texts used throughout the class/schools: standard methods of computation and lay out, used without discrimination and without a measure either of suitability or of understanding.

(iv) The work is not *pupil centred*. It is *teacher centred* in that the teacher is the *authority*; he has to stand for the logical authority of the mathematical principles inherent in a given situation. In turn, the teacher is pressurised by external influences — examination syllabuses, parental and other social pressures.

Contrast with this the essence of the 'New Approach'

(a) Rote learning of symbol manipulation is replaced by work arising from the *experiences of the pupil*. Such experiences may well be of physical entities, particularly in the earlier stages; but they can also be on the pencil/paper sort or even, in the higher stages, of second or higher order concepts derived from earlier experiences. **The repetitive element cannot be eliminated — it is used much more discreetly, economically and purposively.**

(b) From the situation, often contrived by the teacher, the pupil, under unobtrusive guidance, and often skilful questioning, extracts the relevant data, and then expresses it in a suitable form leading to *meaningful symbolism* which he learns to manipulate in a *meaningful* and purposive way.

(c) This type of working grips and fires the imagination of the pupil. The 'chores' of mathematics become more acceptable to him.

(d) The controlled and responsible freedom of the pupil demands a much more permissive classroom atmosphere and a much more discursive approach. The pupil is invited to think for himself and to some extent to design and control his actions: he is encouraged to talk about his mathematics both with his teacher and with his companions.

School and classroom action based on these premises will have a very different flavour from that outlined under the traditional approach, in particular:

(i) Treating the pupil as an individual removes the necessity for streaming, and also the need for much time devoted to 'mass instruction'. Individual or group working is used rather than treating a class as the inevitable unit of instruction.

(ii) The presence and use of physical materials makes demands on storage and working spaces very different from those of a conventional classroom. A workshop is used, hence the need and demand for mathematics laboratories at all levels of mathematics learning.

(iii) The standard text is to some extent replaced by assignment cards supported by an appropriate classroom reference library. Who could hope to find a standard text book suitable for such a group of mixed ability? The classroom library should contain a range of texts to supply such repetitive drill material as is deemed apt at various age and ability levels, it would certainly encourage the use of such textbooks as reference books.

(iv) Motivation is *intrinsic*, in that the work springs from the interests and the desire of the *pupil* to proceed with it. A caveat must be entered here. The foregoing statement does not imply a disorderly 'free for all' or 'a take it or leave it attitude' — it places an even greater responsibility on the environment, and the right kind of stimulation, to ensure that the work proceeds towards desired goals, even though it can rightly be called pupil centred.

In presenting this picture of black and white, the intervening shades of grey must not be overlooked. The two cases represent extremes of an approach continuum. The numbers of teachers in each extreme class are probably relatively small, but there can be little doubt that the distribution is heavily skewed towards the traditional end of the continuum.

Even if it is agreed that some unanimity in approach is thought desirable and possible, the consideration of the content of a course raises issues which rule out the possibility or desirability of a completely common content. Apart from a well defined numerical common core, the field of mathematics available is so large that selection must, of necessity, be made. The criteria to be employed in making a selection are open to some discussion; the following would appear to be some valid criteria to adopt.

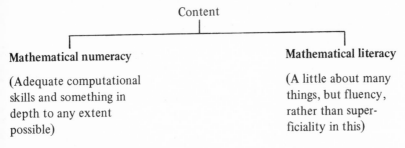

Content

Mathematical numeracy

(Adequate computational skills and something in depth to any extent possible)

Mathematical literacy

(A little about many things, but fluency, rather than super-ficiality in this)

Fig. 2

Fig. 2 suggests a simultaneous advance on two fronts labelled mathematical numeracy and mathematical literacy. The first of these is likely to provide a common core, as a reasonable degree of numeracy is an unquestionably desirable acquisition in all communities; **we should be failing in our duty to the pupil and to society if we do not establish an acceptable degree of numeracy.** In the past, the fact that numeracy is a tool with which to shape mathematics has been under-played, resulting in arid and somewhat tedious courses, lacking in either mathematical content or interest to the less gifted pupils, and consisting only in the acquisition of numerical skills. Even when the skills have been acquired, and this is doubtful for many of the less gifted pupils, rarely were they put to work in making and investigating mathematics itself. As in the past, it may well be that a direct attack on innumeracy will be doomed to failure, and so an indirect attack on the problem should be employed. It is here that the mathematical literacy front can be expected to feed back to the numeracy front. It is this mathematical literacy front which may be expected to provide the spread of courses; for mathematical literacy, in the sense meant, not only includes the language of mathematics but also an appreciation of mathematical patterns and applications of mathematics which are felt to be relevant to the world of today.

The content selected must remain a matter for considered local action always bearing in mind the points:

1. The environment of the school and its relation to the community.

2. The educational ethos of the school.

3. The content should be geared to the age, ability and interests of the individual pupil.

21

More precise suggestions will be found in:
Mathematics for the Majority (1c), and in
Mathematics in Primary Schools (4b).

Conclusion

What then should we expect from a combination of sound modern approach combined with content which the pupil finds interesting and relevant? In general it amounts to a satisfying education which uses mathematics as one of its instruments.

Finale quoted from *Half Our Future* (4a) 'Our aim in the teaching of mathematics to all pupils, to those of average and below average ability no less than to those with marked academic talent, should be to bring them to an interest in the content of mathematics itself at however modest a level'.
... 'Teachers must have a sympathetic understanding for the interest, needs and difficulties of their pupils, and a thirst for experiment in finding and exploiting mathematical situations which arise in the pupils' daily experience.'

References

1. (a) *The Teachers' Guides of the Nuffield Mathematics Project* (5-13) (Murray/Chambers.1967)

   (b) *Texts, guides and materials of the Madison Project* (U.S.A.) (Addison Wesley. 1964)

   (c) *Mathematics for the Majority* Working Paper No. 14 (H.M.S.O. for the Schools Council. 1967)

2. (a) (A series of pupil texts based on the work of a group of Glasgow teachers).

   Mathematics for Schools – A Modern Approach (Foulsham. 1967)

   (b) (A series of pupil texts with accompanying work books based on the work of a group of Devonshire Teachers)

   Making Mathematics Paling, Banwell and Saunders (Oxford University Press. 1968)

   (c) *Mathematics – The Four Year Programme* (Ontario Curriculum Institute in co-operation with the Ontario Mathematics Commission. 1965)

From the Ontario Institute for Studies in Education, 102 Bloor Street West, Toronto 5, Ontario, Canada.

3. *Mathematics and the Conditions of Learning* J. B. Biggs (National Foundation for Educational Research in England & Wales. 1967)

4. (a) *Half Our Future* (The Newsom Report) (H.M.S.O. 1963)

   (b) *Mathematics in Primary Schools* Curriculum Bulletin No. 1 (H.M.S.O. for the Schools Council. 1965)

A Short Book List

1. *Mathematics − A Cultural Approach* Morris Kline (Addison Wesley. 1962)

2. *Teaching General Mathematics* Max. A. Sobel (Prentice Hall. 1967)

3. *The New Look in Mathematics Teaching* (University of Hull Institute of Education. 1965)

4. *Mathematics Laboratories in Schools* (Bell for the Mathematical Association. 1968)

5. *Count Me In: Numeracy in Education* Ed. J. T. Combridge (Queen Anne Press. 1968) (A B.P. Progress book)

Part 2

CASE HISTORIES

Prologue

As foreshadowed in the introduction, the case histories that follow have been chosen because they depict how pioneering schools and teachers have in *one way or another* been planning to make mathematical life more relevant and attractive to 'our Pupils'.

It must be emphasised that the case histories were selected from a number available. Our use of some geographically located titles may well lead you to ask 'Cannot the counterparts of such work be found elsewhere – in Wales, in East Anglia, in the Midlands, in the North West?' The considered reply is 'They certainly can'. In short, there is no pecking order in the selection. Lively work is welcomed *wherever* it occurs.

In a very real sense these are historical documents from workers early in the field, and we think it proper that they should be presented to you as they occurred, and with the imperial units of measurement which were then employed. This is our reason for non-metrication of the units; and so this book will differ in this respect from the other books of the series.

Consequently it is essential that if any of this work is to form the basis of pupil assignments, the teachers concerned must make the necessary adjustments in order to comply with the metric system of money, weights and measures.

That many of the practices described exemplify some of the ideas put forward in Part I is a matter of selection and not one of collaborative writing. None of the schools concerned *began* with any advantages either of environment or of equipment; the outcomes described are the results of imaginative planning together with patient and determined action on the part of the teachers concerned and of their colleagues. Almost all of the action took place in the 'rectangular box', classroom, unhappily now regarded as the inevitable shape; but a measure of mathematics outside the class and the classroom will be noted also.

While these ideas and experiments are certainly not put out as models for all to copy, it might well be that they could help teachers to prepare the ground, particularly with regard to the approach to the pupils' learning, in readiness for the more content-based books to follow. Such is our hope.

THE NEW YORK PROJECT
(see p. 29)

3

Mathematics Outside the Classroom

The first four years of a Mathematics Club

Mathematics Club X, an out-of-school club of a coeducational secondary modern school of five hundred pupils, is now in its fifth year. The school itself is ten years old, and started its life with an intake of first and second year pupils. When the Mathematics Club was formed it had no tradition in the subject of mathematics, and the Club was an attempt to give added depth and interest to the subject. It is true to say that not only has it achieved these aims, but, further, it has killed any fear that mathematics often produces in the young; the pupils in the school, on the whole, enjoy the subject in a way they probably would not had the club never existed.

The Club meets twice a week, reduced to once a week when public examinations loom. It operates from 4 p.m. to 5.15 p.m., although the latter is rather elastic, and on one occasion the meeting carried on till 6.45 without anyone being aware of the time. Its inception was haphazard, and but for some strokes of good fortune this might have led to its early demise. Small project work was carried out, described later, and this was unsatisfactory for many reasons, the chief of which was that these projects did not supply enough work to keep everyone busy. This led to the introduction of several projects at the same time, and this was taxing the ingenuity of the teacher and extremely expensive; only the idea of big projects saved the Club from extinction.

The school caters for pupils of from rather above average to below average ability and the first Club members were the elite, academically, of this cross-section. This is almost inevitable and fortunately so, as from the outset the standards are high. It would not be so fortunate if it opened a gulf that those of below average ability, following on, could not cross; but the fact is that the latter maintain these standards and demand the same vision. They become indistinguishable from their fellow members in the routine jobs, and their involvement can be judged by the immense amount of pride they take in the end-product.

From the outset it was decided to apply no pressure concerning membership, and the Club had to stand or fall on the capability of the subject to generate interest. No time-limit was set to attendance at a meeting; it was the member's right to come at any time and leave at any time, five minutes later if he, or she, so desired. This was done to allay the feeling of being 'trapped' and thus to encourage those of below average ability who might attend. After a few meetings membership hardened to half-a-dozen faithfuls and floating three or four, all from A and B streams. For nearly two terms nobody from a C stream attended. Finally, after big project work had been introduced, one C stream boy asked if he might come and watch. When it was pointed out that he was at perfect liberty not only to watch but to join in, he grew panicky, and this line was quickly discontinued. He came, watched, joined in, and had a very good time, and brought practically the whole class to the next meeting.

As the years have rolled by, membership has increased to about twenty-five regulars and an equal number of floaters. The C stream proportion is good.

The numerous small projects which were entered upon in the early days of the Club included curve-stitching, design of houses and plans, the design and construction of an elaborate harmonograph, Boolean circuitry, and the construction of simple two-way reverse circuits, memory systems, including storage and extraction, three-dimensional games, and coding and de-coding. Technical drawing was closely allied to most of the projects, and designs were taken seriously; everything constructed came from a blueprint. Not all these projects were ultimately successful, but the path to failure was enjoyable, and the pupils learned much.

With the advent of the big project idea came relief from the organisational nightmare that had built up with increased membership, little cash, and a drying up of inspiration.

Alan C's father was trying to sell a 16 mm Bell and Howell movie camera and it was suggested that this be hired to make a film. It was decided to make a film on Conic Sections in colour, using trick photography to build up the diagrams. The Club members, including the teacher, were completely ignorant of the techniques involved, but information began to pour in from members, using their libraries to good account, from parents who heard of the idea and were interested, and from the treasurer of the local photographic society, who was promptly roped in as Honorary Consultant. Strangely enough in spite of this wealth of information, the more important techniques that were mastered came, not from information received, but rather from a process of trial and error. For example, the diagrams were built up, a few frames at a time, by lines and dots cut from sticky paper; it took a long time for even one diagram to be filmed, and it was very tedious sticking on another three dots without causing the slightest movement to the hardboard base. The first fifty feet of film to be processed revealed many unexpected flaws; the base was moving slightly, in spite of our efforts; the new dots, recently added, because they were wet were a different colour from the dots where the glue had dried; some lines grew too quickly, others grew too slowly, and worst of all, dots that were not placed exactly in the correct position ruined the symmetry. This last problem was very difficult to overcome, as one's head angled when putting on the dots, and it was impossible to be more accurate using the technique that was being employed. The problem was solved by a Club member suggesting that the process be reversed. The figure would be built up before it came in front of the camera, and would, therefore, be absolutely accurate. Then instead of gradually being built up, it would be gradually dismantled in front of the camera, and the film taken, showing a break down, could be reversed to show a build up. Somebody else suggested that tape dots would then be preferable to paper ones as they would peel off easily. The filmed results of these modifications were superb, and quite professional. The build up of diagrams away from the camera meant that several diagrams could be executed at the same time, and this provided jobs for all. Teams worked on the more intricate models, the simpler ones being built by individuals. A tremendous amount was learnt of the properties of conic sections, mathematically, and of the techniques employed in sketching them. No project undertaken, before or after, conic sections was even half so educationally successful. On the debit side however, was the expense involved, and this continually menaced the project. The film was eventually completed, and was shown several times to the School, causing a rise in membership of the Club.

'If you were on the twentieth floor of a building in New York and looked out of the window, what would you see?' This was the theme of the New York project that followed-up the conic sections. It was to be an exercise involving skyline architecture, perspective and scale-modelling; and constructionally it fell into three parts. Firstly, a sky must be constructed to give an infinity of depth, and this would be like looking into the inside half of a very large eggshell. If a square window were built into the circular cross-section, the eye of the beholder would lose its point of reference and the depth, if perfectly smooth and painted with light blue matt paint, would achieve an impression of infinity. Secondly, scale model buildings had to be constructed in perspective, and this involved some very interesting practical mathematics to determine the angles of perspective. The architectural design of the buildings, and their effect on the skyline, was taken seriously, and no blue print was accepted until it had been passed by the 'Planning Commission'. Thirdly, the resulting model required lighting effects of a high order. It was soon discovered that lighting outside the buildings was insufficient to lend an air of reality to the whole. As soon as the lights were placed inside the buildings as well, they came alive. Shadows were everywhere, and had to be removed.

The New York project took a year to complete, and the results were curious and unexpected. The daylight effect (full lighting) conjured up the reality of New York only when viewed from a few positions. From most positions, the model was just a model. Fortunately, however, the circuit permitted the switching off of main lights, leaving on the lights inside the building. It was summer when the model was completed, with no blackout facilities in the classroom, and so the significance of this lighting arrangement (a pure fluke) was not appreciated. At 6 p.m. on an autumn day when it was dark both inside and outside the classroom, somebody switched on the building lights of the model. The result was fantastic; it achieved absolute reality, the glow of the buildings, the dark sky, the diaphanous quality of the lighting as a whole; reality in any position, whether moving or standing still.

The successor to this project, as yet unfinished, has been the Fingerprints project. This project calls for classification from the results of calculation and very accurate measuring, using specialised instruments.

The Club is attempting, from first principles and without any reference to Police methods, to devise a system to classify fingerprints, and then to be able to match them with random prints. The School Science Department is collaborating in chemical techniques of how to treat a print to get the best photographic result possible.

Formation:

In our forward thinking about the formation of a school maths. club we thought that the initial structure should arise out of the following considerations:

It should be social in character, with different disciplines from those to be met within the classroom. For example, the 'insulation' about the teacher in the classroom can be discarded, for it is unnecessary in dealing with pupils who are voluntary members and can come or go as they wish. Again, it is the Club, as a whole, that demands work to be completed, not the teacher. It quite often happens that the Club wishes to complete a piece of work when the teacher is not in the mood and with a firmly based club it is the teacher who will give way. In other words, a good club builds up a 'dynamic' that carries it through the less interesting, but necessary, work. Nagging or persuasive methods by the teacher will fall through in the long run.

The work carried out must be exciting, with a clearly visible end-product, although, strangely enough, it does not seem to matter a great deal if this end-product, when reached, is disappointing. Projects, exciting along the way, which ultimately fall down in the last stage (possibly because they were too ambitious) are still looked back on as 'fun' by the pupils who really are most sensible about the question of success or failure. Consequently, in the light of this ability to accept ultimate failure, it is much better to attempt an ambitious, exciting project than to play safe. It may be that the teacher is very uncertain about the ground of a project that has been chosen. He, or she, should state this very clearly to the members. An air of 'We'll work this out together or go down in the attempt' may be questionable in a classroom, but meat and drink in a project. It is free from the classroom that the members have gained confidence in the teacher. They are quite willing to accept his humility in project work, and it gives them the feeling that they are working on frontiers of knowledge, generating the urge that produces all genuine results in research. The laboriousness of certain tasks becomes a labour of love.

The Club should meet as often as possible, at least once a week, or the momentum will be lost.

One teacher must be responsible for the club and be always present. Rotative schemes amongst the teachers of a mathematics department are inviting failure from the start. This provides a soulless community without the vision necessary to see the project through to the end. The vision must be continually presented by its progenitor, and can be used as a spur.

Vertically, the Club must grow downwards from the top of the School. Members of the Vth and IVth forms must be committed before, or at the same time, as members of the lower school. Horizontally, the growth must be from capability to mediocrity and never the reverse; even if the Club be intended primarily for the backward, they (the backward) must be convinced that interesting and valuable work can be accomplished before they will raise their sights, and they will strive to emulate the quality of this work. It would be a misunderstanding of the above if if were assumed that the less gifted child performed inferior tasks. On the contrary, once they too see the vision, and the quality of the craftsmanship of work already completed, they will be as able and useful as any other member.

As stated previously, the work carried out must be exciting. What sort of work? The Club can grow in many directions, some of which are abortive. For example, if a series of small projects, easily accomplished, are embarked upon, the teacher's ingenuity is taxed to the limit to complete even a year's work. This work cannot be re-presented the following year without losing the senior members of the Club. Another unsatisfactory direction of growth is to compartmentalise the Club, for here the teacher is dealing with an octopus. It is better to embark on one grand project that will encompass everyone, and provide jobs for all, and that will take the whole school-year to accomplish. There are good reasons to back this up: firstly, the bigger the project the grander the vision that will sell it; secondly, the teacher becomes a director rather than a conjuror; thirdly, it is very much cheaper to provide material for a large project than a series of smaller ones. Why this latter condition is true is dealt with in the section on Finance.

Large projects are not easy to come by, but a teacher, having launched one, has a whole year to ponder on the next, and in this exercise of the imagination it is not only the pupil who will benefit. This large project, whatever its nature, must have certain ingredients. It must have a basis of mathematics; the end-product, particularly if less able pupils are involved, should be visible and not abstract; it must conform to the budget; and lastly, the most exacting condition, it should contain a bundle of small jobs that will keep all the members (particularly the weaker brethren) fully occupied. In the New York project, mentioned below, the laborious task was the cutting of ten thousand miniature windows, and, no sooner were they cut, a window-cleaning army came into existence. No member was exclusively set to this onerous task. All participated in the more interesting and instructive work, and all cut windows; a fair division of labour was arrived at without any need for organisation . . . another example of the 'dynamic' at work.

Within the context of one grand project per year that after a while begins to run itself, there is room for a limited amount of small project work, particularly in the field of visual aids.

In any large project, subject frontiers are bound to be crossed, but providing that the project has a basis of mathematics this seems all to the good. In the Fingerprints project, the School's Science Department has agreed to act in an analytic capacity — they will sort out the prints into categories; and, in this project, another frontier is crossed in that an extensive use of rather sophisticated photographic techniques has been necessary.

In the formation of the Mathematics Club it is a great temptation to change its name to disguise its essentially mathematical nature. By such a change an initial victory may be won by gaining members more rapidly, including those unsuspecting of any mathematical bias. This surely constitutes lack of faith in a subject that is vital and exciting, and does a great disservice to the image of mathematics within a school. It also cuts across the chief aim of a Mathematics Club, that of ridding the pupil of fear towards the subject and inspiring new confidence.

Aims

In discussing the aims of a Mathematics Club it is as well to be aware of a difference between its short term and long term aims. The immediate aim is to use mathematics to generate such interest that the pupils come back for more, of their own accord. If the pull is not great enough they will not come back in sufficient numbers to popularise the subject, and the view will prevail that mathematics is for the eccentric few. The long term aims, which depend on a flourishing membership with a cross-section that includes both the average and below average pupil, would never be achieved.

The long term aims must surely be to rid children of fear of the subject, to work with enthusiasm and comradeship to the attainment of a new confidence and insight, and to create a 'dynamic' that supplants the disciplines and methods of the classroom. These aims will only be realised in a club that is thriving and oversubscribed in its membership. The vitality will not be achieved quickly, but it will steadily build up if a realistic policy is adopted and if the inevitable mistaken notions are discarded. A method of accelerating this vitality is described below in the section Attainment of Aims, but it represents the view of one teacher only, and is merely food for thought. Different teachers will employ different means and lead their clubs in different directions.

Attainment of Aims

Bound up with the introduction of a project is a minds-eye view of what it will be when it is completed. The exploitation of this 'dream' of finalisation is as important to the Organiser of a Mathematics Club as it is to an estate agent. The dream sells the project and generates the initial interest that encourages the member to attend the next meeting. As the project gets under way it will begin to create its own interest (the satisfaction of 'doing' rather than of anticipating) and the dream will be replaced by the reality. The dream binds existing members to the Club; the reality adds new ones.

The dream is important, and its saleability must affect the choice of the project. Because of this, visible end-products are to be preferred, generally, to the abstract. However, in the case of a project (such as an abstract one) where the 'dream' is a weak feature, it can be strengthened by tying the end-product up with an event. For example the end-product will be displayed (or demonstrated) to parents and visitors on Open Day, etc.

This idea was used successfully to bolster the Fingerprints project where the end-product was abstract. The 'dream' was greatly strengthened when it was suggested that a team of Scotland Yard experts be challenged to a fingerprints contest on the School stage, during the annual fete. The challenge has, as yet, not been sent out as the project is unfinished; but the Yard have a sense of humour, and it is just conceivable that they might agree to take part in a bit of light-hearted entertainment.

Finance

Small projects gobble up money, and, as they last but a short time, are difficult to allow for in any pre-planned budget. Pre-planning is surely the secret of financial success in the Mathematics Club, and this can only mean the big project, thought of a year in advance with three hundred and sixty five days to scrape together the material required initially, and almost double that time to amass the finishing materials.

Where does the money come from to pay for these items? With pre-planning two important sources of revenue can be tapped. The first is the obvious one of ordering material required through funds of the School's mathematics department. The order is not for current project, but for its successor. The second is the keeping of a register of parents, who with their goodwill and by nature of their employment are able to help. The tactful approach to being able to enter a parent's name in the register itself requires a degree of pre-planning. For example, Willie Smith, a Club member has a dad who is a painter. At Prize-giving, or on some convenient occasion, during conversation father is asked whether he can lend any assistance in the matter of paint. If he feels that the Mathematics Club is serving any useful purpose in his son's life, it may well be that paint, in the future of the Club, will be a deductable item.

In the New York project, the shell had been constructed but had to have a perfectly smooth interior. Nobody, the teacher least of all, could think of any other medium than plaster to achieve this; but this meant plastering a surface that was round in cross-section and elliptical in depth, a plastering nightmare to all but a skilled professional decorator. However, Eddie's father, a registered parent, was a professional decorator and he not only gave of his time and skill, which was an education in itself to watch, but he also gave freely of his plaster. It is certain that he derived as much satisfaction from the completion of the project as his son did.

Most important, the will to succeed will always, somehow or other, generate the necessary cash.

Conclusion

It has been stated earlier in this article that the Mathematics Club referred to was formed, in a school that had no tradition in the subject, as an attempt to give added depth and interest. This aim has been genuinely accomplished; but a great deal more has also been accomplished that was unforeseen at its inception. Firstly, it has bred a confidence in the subject that has undoubtedly infected even those pupils who have never attended a meeting, and the latter take a sort of 'remote control' pride in the club.

The pupils have been refreshed with the knowledge that mathematics can be used, by them, to achieve a visible end-product. This has always been one of the great mysteries, that bubbles to the surface at times with questions such as 'I like doing these equations, but what are they useful for?' and now the mystery is solved to their own satisfaction. It is true to say that from this time onwards they never look at the subject in the same way again. They really begin to believe in mathematics instead of suffering it.

Secondly, and this is a direct consequence of what has gone before, a confidence will be bred in them towards their teachers. This influence is subtle and more difficult to measure, but it is best judged by their greater flexibility in facing the challenge of fresh aspects of the subject. This may be taken as a vote of confidence in the teacher in leading them to this part of the jungle, as being the shortest route to the promised land. The journey is easier because they have already had a glimpse of it, and believe in its existence.

Some changes are very gradual and pass almost unnoticed. A parent has to look at a year-old photograph to realise the growth of his own off-spring, in the same way it is difficult to assess a change in classroom discipline and attitude in the teaching of a subject. It has been mentioned earlier that the teacher's approach to a Mathematics Club may be different from his approach in the classroom. The teacher may wear two faces. There is a case to be made for a Mathematics Club in that very thought alone; he needs the Club to develop the second (and all-important) 'face'. It is the product of an unorthodox approach, combined with a deliberate change of status with respect to the pupils. Having achieved this second 'face' in the relaxed atmosphere of the Club, it is not to be put aside, for it carries too many advantages over the former. Gradually (perhaps unconsciously) the two faces come together. This metamorphosis, noticable from a distance, is built up so slowly from period to period that it passes unnoticed in the classroom. The pupils do not realise that once they were in opposition to the teacher; they have come to regard him as on their side in the contest, a trainer of the team.

4

Action in the South East

The publication of Working Paper No. 14 *Mathematics for the Majority*, by the Schools Council sets out the basis of a three year programme to discover what mathematics might best be taught to the majority of secondary school pupils.

There has been much progress in the past decade both in teaching method and syllabus content and much good has derived from the many excellent projects such as the Schools Mathematics Project, the Midlands Mathematical Experiment and the work of the Scottish Mathematics Group. These gains, however, have largely been concerned with the more able pupils. The title of the Working Paper highlights a need of which I am sure many of my colleagues who are teaching in the secondary modern schools are well aware. Most teachers will concede the need to change the method in teaching subjects in the contemporary schools situation. Progress in the approach through individual study and practice and relevance to the modern world is undeniable. But many teachers are unable to see how the new methods can be organised within the real situation of the classroom.

There is in the secondary schools less conviction of the need to change the material content of the syllabus. It is true that some 'new' mathematics is being taught; the binary system and the concepts of set theory are good examples, but the conviction remains that most of the content of past syllabuses is still relevant. Beyond this, the realisation has grown that the syllabus must be in touch with what might be called 'the stream of mathematics consciousness' and in particular that the false division created by dividing mathematics into separate subjects must be closed.

It was with these thoughts in mind that we set up our first mathematics workshop just twelve months ago, after some preliminary skirmishes in the previous two terms. We started with one first-year class of mixed ability in January 1967. Since September 1967 the experiment has been broadened to include all first and second year classes.

A brief outline of the background is relevant to a closer understanding of the experiment.

We are a three form entry school situated in a pilot area for the Nuffield Mathematics project (5-13). Our intake is of very mixed experience of mathematics teaching, about one third coming from the

'Nuffield' area and the remainder from country and smalltown primary schools.

The school has not been streamed for the past five years; all classes are of mixed ability. Mathematics is 'set' in the upper school but we have now abolished mathematics 'sets' in the first and second year classes.

We have a strong academic tradition in the fifth and sixth year classes and a high record of academic achievement for a secondary modern school. We make this point to show that we are a successful school in these terms and unlikely therefore to join any 'band-wagon' of current trend simply for the sake of it.

These are the fundamental aims and principles of the scheme.

1. It was decided to retain mixed-ability classes for mathematics lessons for the first two years of the secondary school.

2. We accepted the principle of individual work and *no* class teaching with the experimental class.

3. The syllabus was broadly outlined and revised to include some of the 'modern' topics which had previously been tried with various teaching groups.

4. The material was presented in a logical sequence in the form of individual worksheets so that each pupil was able to understand the written instructions and to learn the appropriate mathematical language at the same time.

5. The onus of learning was passed to the individual pupil so that gradually he might proceed to the ultimate state of selflearning. This change freed the teacher from class-teaching so that the individual might consult him whenever the need arose.

6. The use of apparatus, wall charts and any other aids was encouraged to assist pupils to learn mathematics by building up concepts from their own concrete experiences.

The Workshop

A small classroom was converted into a workshop although each lesson necessitated an overspill into an adjoining corridor. We tried to make the room a place for practical mathematical experiences where investigations of problems raised could be carried out: a place of interest where pupils would be moved to discover and would feel encouraged to ask questions. There were three short weeks in the Christmas holidays to prepare the first wall charts, the early pieces of apparatus required, the first couple of dozen worksheets. Some slight modifications of the room were made to create additional display areas on the walls and around the windows.

The furniture consisted of some flat topped tables for working surfaces, an old desk converted to a woodwork bench, a working table for cutting card, a store cupboard, book shelves, shelving for displaying models, and peg board.

A small initial outlay of money was necessary to equip the workshop with tools, instruments, equipment and a stock of materials.

The Outline of the Syllabus

The syllabus can perhaps best be followed by looking at the flow diagram (Fig. 3) and referring to the notes on the worksheets. In order to keep the need for duplicating apparatus and charts to a minimum, the syllabus has been arranged in four parallel columns (each of which soon becomes very much related with the others). On entry, pupils are given different starting points so as to allow a spread of activity. Experience has shown that differences in individual rates of progress soon take care of any problem of crowding which might result. We believe that mathematical ideas and concepts need to be met at regular intervals and with as many different experiences as possible. Therefore the worksheets are numbered so that pupils move horizontally across the flow diagram as well as vertically downwards.

The Worksheets

In making the worksheet the main vehicle of communication of mathematical material, it is obviously important to make the work of each sheet a valuable mathematical experience which the pupil will understand and enjoy. Whenever possible some piece of mathematical apparatus or aid is thought out to help form the particular mathematical concept. The sheet is a direct and personal communication between the individual pupil and the teacher.

The worksheets are arranged in four groups, A, B, C, D, each group starting with a different topic. See flow diagram Fig. 3.

Answer cards for each sheet are immediately available to the pupil when he completes a sheet. The pupil corrects his own answers and raises with the teacher any problem which gives him difficulty where his answer differs from that given on the answer card.

After four or five worksheets on a particular topic have been successfully completed, there is a short test paper which is marked by the teacher. This forms the basis of any necessary teaching points for individual pupils and keeps the teacher in close contact with the progress of each pupil.

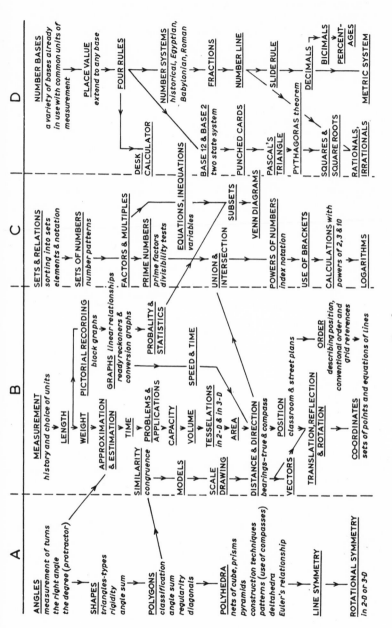

Fig. 3.

Pupils will thus meet worksheets in this sort of order:

1A, 2A, 3A, 4A, Test 1 (Work on Angles), followed by:
1B, 2B, 3B, 4B, Test 2 (Work on Length), followed by:
1C, 2C, 3C, 4C, Test 3 (Work on Sets), followed by:
1D, 2D, 3D, 4D, Test 4 (Work on Number bases), followed by:
5A, 6A, 7A, 8A, Test 5 (Brief recap. on Angles and extension to next topic) and so on.

On reflection we think that some of the early work should begin at an earlier age (10+). We are aware that the worksheets might not appear as 'open ended' as many present-day schemes, but we have in mind that most of our children are unlikely to discover very much mathematics unless they are led right to the brink.

Recording individual progress creates no problem. At the completion of each work sheet, the pupil enters the worksheet number and the date on a master sheet so that at any time the teacher knows exactly what each pupil is doing.

Conclusions

At the end of the summer term we gave the 'experimental' class the same test as the two 'control' classes who had continued with formal class-teaching. We thought that the test was heavily biased in favour of the 'controls' in that it was a formal-type examination containing quite an amount of work that the 'experimental' class had not tackled. The results showed that:

(a) **The top third of each of the three classes gained almost identical marks.**

(b) **The middle third of the 'experimental' class gained slightly more marks than the corresponding pupils in the 'control'.**

(c) **The bottom third of the 'experimental' class were way above their counterparts in the other two classes, i.e. the long tail of 'non-mathematicians' had almost disappeared.**

Here are a few further reflections made in July, 1967:

The Pupils

(a) After two terms they were still enthusiastic and willing to work. They much preferred the active participation in the lesson rather than the passive listening, and the use of apparatus added interest to their work.

(b) They were more willing to accept the 'chores' of the subject.

(c) Only now were they beginning to understand many of the fundamental concepts which previously we had taken for granted.

(d) As a direct result of a quite remarkable percentage of success in the tests, there was a general increase in confidence and a willingness to tackle further problems.

(e) The backward readers showed a marked improvement in reading and all became far more confident in using mathematical terminology.

(f) The more-able pupils did not want the teacher to interfere unless they were in real difficulty.

(g) The majority preferred to work as individuals rather than in pairs or small groups.

(h) In spite of far greater periods of concentration (I estimate that the majority of the class are hard at work for about 80% of each double period), the tendency was to cover work at a slower rate than under the system of class-teaching. I think this probably emphasises the point that many of us try to cover too much ground too quickly!

(i) The quality of the work was astonishingly high. They seemed to take a great pride in their exercise books and all were perfectly presentable at an 'open-day' for parents in spite of the fact that I had not marked any work in them at all. (The tests were done on separately prepared sheets.)

The Teacher

There was a vastly improved pupil-teacher relationship. The teacher becomes a person to whom all are willing to go for help. The shy or backward pupil who might never have asked a question or volunteered an answer in the class situation, loses his fear of ridicule from his fellow pupils and participates quite naturally in a friendly relationship with the teacher.

It is in this relationship that true learning will flourish as a result of successful communication between pupil and teacher.

Some people have charitably described any form of freedom in the classroom as 'organised chaos'. Of course it requires a short period of time for weaning pupils to accept freedom and informality in place of rigid control. However, if discipline is present, there is no need for any sign of 'chaos' when pupils are all working individually and the amount of noise in the workshop is inversely proportional to the interest that the worksheet generates.

There was a large decrease in the amount of time spent on unnecessary marking – the only marking undertaken was the test papers which were marked in the presence of the pupil if humanly possible.

It seemed that some group-feeling was missed through there being no time given to talking to the class as a whole. This has since been rectified and some ten minute periods during longer mathematics lessons each week are devoted to some topic of general interest (e.g. some aspect of 'Modern' mathematics or homework) which does not appear in the worksheets. Otherwise the full three double periods per week are spent on individual work.

Whilst it is preferable to have a mathematics specialist, we have found it very easy for a non-specialist to take over a class working individually. A further alternative is for a specialist and a non-specialist to work together with two classes and so employ a system of team-teaching.

The Future

(a) The initial amount of work to set up this system was quite phenomenal: to date we have prepared material for about two and a half years and this includes some 250 foolscap worksheets and a vast amount of apparatus, wall charts and equipment to go with them. We are beginning to see daylight and have begun to amend and rewrite some of our early effort as a result of further experience.

(b) We have in mind that we require to expand our efforts to fulfil the need for more 'parallel experience' worksheets to provide repetition of each mathematical experience in as many different fields as possible.

(c) Since September, 1967 we have been fortunate enough to move into a very large room and have now completed our Workshop Mark II. The scheme has been extended to the whole of the first and second year pupils and a further two masters have given it their full support.

(d) A full year has passed since the original scheme was launched and it has steadily gained impetus so that we find it difficult to predict where it will end. With comprehensive education just around the corner, perhaps our efforts will need to be used to take into account the even wider range of ability that we might expect. Or, perhaps, we shall feel that an extension of the idea further up the age range of the school is imperative.

Whichever way we move, the vast amount of work involved has been well and truly balanced by the tremendous satisfaction that we have so far gained from what started as a small experiment in the teaching-learning process.

5

Action in the North East

The episodes which follow form part of the education of the pupils in our co-educational non-selective (secondary modern) school of some thousand pupils. These pupils are contained within five year groups. In each of the first four years we have three streamed classes geared to public examinations, some for G.C.E. (O Level) and others for C.S.E. The remaining pupils in each year are unstreamed and work in mixed ability forms. Although each of these unstreamed forms has an ability range from middle B to D they play a significant part in the mathematical work and life of the school.

It is no exaggeration to say that the hub of the mathematical work of this school is a space of dimensions 48 ft by 24 ft. This space, a rather large former classroom, provides us with our mathematics laboratory, allowing ample space both for practical activities and for display purposes. Within its walls we have been able to provide facilities for model making, a number of woodwork benches with appropriate tools, and a puzzle corner where the pupils can profitably engage in sundry mathematical inconsequences found in a series of puzzle sheets provided there. A sample puzzle sheet is shown later. The mathematics laboratory also provides the venue for year-group meetings which are a feature of our current mathematical approach. These will be described in greater detail later. Classroom work is conducted in rooms situated in close proximity to the mathematics laboratory, and in addition we have been able to get a small room which we have set aside for private study. So much then for the environment in which our pupils learn mathematics.

Within the framework just outlined, we try to involve each pupil in as many and as varied manifestations of mathematics as are meaningful to him at his particular level of ability. To this end we aim at variety in learning situations, dealing variously with large groups (a year group) with small groups (form teaching) and with individual assignments planned for a pupil.

Work with all the unstreamed forms is conducted in the following manner, but we write here specifically of work with the unstreamed fourth year pupils. A member of staff dealing with the mathematics of these fourth year pupils prepares and delivers a lecture to the whole of the fourth year unstreamed group in the presence of his colleagues who are

43

similarly concerned with these pupils. This lecture, which takes place in the mathematics laboratory, provides the centre piece for the unit of work to be undertaken by the fourth year pupils for a variable number of periods.

Careful pre-planning of time and topic not only enables the lecturer to prepare his material thoroughly, but it enables him to consider the details of its presentation to the particular audience at which it is aimed; it also allows time for consideration and use of the available supporting services such as films, film strips, tape recorder, duplicated sheets or it may perhaps be a rather more specialised piece of equipment such as a binary adder. It has sometimes happened that one of the lecture topics was the particular interest of a particular member of staff, in which case the choice of lecturer was automatic, and we could be reasonably sure of a lively and authoritative lecture, presented from a varied and rich background. This then is our work with the large group unit.

From the inception of this scheme, we realised that the large group lecture was not of itself the complete learning situation — it needed support in a smaller group structure. After each lecture therefore the members of staff take their groups to their respective classrooms and develop the lecture in their own ways. In this way the personality and individuality of the teacher is expressed, and in like manner the form personality and group interests of the pupils can be catered for. This second phase of the operation pursues the content of the lecture to greater depths and it sometimes explores side issues which emerge from the lecture; it also provides opportunity for the fixing of whatever principles and skills are contained in the work. This second phase lasts until such time as by discussion and mutual agreement of the staff concerned, it is felt that the time is ripe to open up a fresh and preferably a different topic, in which case the stages of the operation are repeated.

Topics already covered in the fourth year include:

Number bases, including binary number and Codes (messages are sent by tom tom across the school yard and we eagerly await the invention, by an imaginative group of pupils, of a smoke signalling system).
Sets and Venn diagrams
Odds and Chance
Permutations
Decimal Coinage
Graphs — their construction and interpretation

In addition to this lecture/classroom approach we bring the fourth year pupils into close involvement with other facets of mathematics. For example, they use the physical facilities of the mathematics room for model making, apparatus making, curve stitching and use of desk calculators. The puzzle corner already mentioned is a perpetual source of

44

fascination and interest to the pupils. Here is one of the puzzle sheets we have made.

PUZZLE SHEET NO. 1

1. Two ducks in front of a duck; two ducks behind a duck, and a duck in the middle. How many ducks were there?

2. There are twelve pennies in a dozen. How many halfpennies are there?

3. What is the largest sum of money a man may have in his pocket and yet not be able to change a ten-shilling note? (all coins being silver).

4. One train leaves London for Edinburgh at 2.10 a.m. travelling at 40 m.p.h. A second train leaves Edinburgh for London half an hour later travelling at 45 m.p.h. When they meet, which is the nearer to London?

5. A clock takes 6 seconds to strike six. How long will it take to strike eleven?

6. Can you make fourpence of two coins, one of which is not a 3d bit?

7. In the following sequences can you tell which number is out of step?

(i)	1,8,27,63	(iv)	1,3,6,10,16
(ii)	2,4,7,16	(v)	1,5,14,29,55
(iii)	3,5,7,9,15		

8. What is the next number in the following sequences?

(i) 1,16,81,256............................

(ii) 1,3,6,10,15............................

(iii) 1,9,35,91...............................

(iv) 7,5,21,19,43,41.......................

9. Mr. Slumber retired to his study the other afternoon at three o'clock as he had so much work to do. He settled himself comfortably in his armchair and when he first glanced at the clock, he noted that the hands of the clock were exactly together. What was the time?

10. In the diagram overleaf, the last square of the row bears some definite relationship to the first two. You are asked to complete the ninth square.

11. Using four fours and any recognised mathematical signs that you wish, make up the following:

(i) 15   (ii) 24   (iii) 44   (iv) 36

(For example 16 = 4 + 4 + 4 + 4.)

45

1	6
2	1

3	2
5	7

4	8
7	8

7	2
6	4

4	3
7	5

11	5
13	9

8	8
8	5

7	5
12	12

12. The following conversation occurred when I went into a shop and asked the price of certain articles, which, I was told, were 2d each. 'So 100 will cost me sixpence?' 'That's right, Sir' 'I will take 86 please' 'That will be 4d plear Sir'. WHAT WAS I BUYING?

Or again, two questions from the sheet headed:

SORT THEM OUT

(a) A General, an Admiral and an Air Marshal, named White, Brown and Green (but not respectively) are all members of the same club. White, Brown and Green are servants all of the club.

(i) Green earns one-seventh as much as his namesake.

(ii) The Air Marshall earns £2468 per annum.

(iii) The Admiral beat Brown's namesake at snooker.

(iv) The Air-Marshal dislikes his namesake but gave Brown a handsome tip at Christmas.
What are the names of the General, the Admiral and the Air-Marshall?

(b) Three men, Hill, Hall and Hull were by profession doctor, docker

46

and dentist (not respectively) and one was by hobby a philatelist, one an ornithologist, and the other a campanologist.

(i) Hill lives halfway between the dentist and the philatelist.

(ii) Hull visits the dentist professionally.

(iii) Hall beat the ornithologist at darts.
What are the hobbies of the three men?

During the summer term all third and fourth year unstreamed classes study elementary surveying. Using unsophisticated apparatus, sometimes made by the pupils themselves, they find the heights of buildings and carry out simple surveys by triangulation and by offset methods. We have gradually built up a sufficient supply of simple surveying equipment to enable us to have a whole year of pupils out at any given time.

The surveying equipment is put to further use in the study of a historic castle situated within easy reach of the school. After preparation, which involves the close co-operation of the history, geography and mathematics departments of the school, the pupils visit the castle for a substantial period and work individually or in small groups using assignment sheets. Typical questions with a mathematical content include:

1. Number of steps leading up to the door in the Castle Keep ....
2. Approximate height of one step is..........
3. Therefore height of door above the ground is..........
4. Check your answer to number 3 by measurement..........
5. Now count the number of stones up the height of the Castle..........
6. Find the average height of a stone.
7. Therefore height of castle by this method is..........
8. Height of Castle by 45° set square method is..........
9. Go to the top of the Castle. Lower a piece of string with stone attached over the side, other member of group hold string taut at foot of castle. Find height thus by actual measurement of string on ground.
10. From top of castle estimate:
    (i) Distance of Hilton Hotel.
    (ii) Distance of water tower.
    (iii) Distance of power station.
11. Check your answers to number 10 from a map, when you return to school.

The material whether mathematical, geographical or historical, so collected on the visit is brought back to school and provides the main content of a project study undertaken by the Fourth year pupils.

Another venture which can now be fairly claimed to have achieved the status of an annual event is the *Money Conference*.

Preparations are made months before the money conference. Pupils learn about percentages, interest, simple and compound and like matters.

At the actual conference, which takes place in an afternoon we have:

(a) A Bank Manager

(b) A District Commissioner for National Savings.

(c) A Building Society Manager.

Each pupil is issued with a stencilled programme for the afternoon.

They will see that each guest speaks in turn about his particular dealings with money.

After a break for refreshments, pupils ask questions of the speakers as in a formal meeting.

Preparations are made beforehand so that the usual silence when asked for 'any questions' is overcome. The usual way of obtaining questions is to make sure when teaching the pupils about banks and money matters, prior to the conference, that we avoid covering all that the pupils wish to know. Pupils then start asking questions and we ask them to write them down on a piece of paper along with their name. The reason given is that a person will be coming who can answer the questions more fully and accurately than we can. By this method we have found that there is no lack of questions and the conference has been known to go on until nearly 5 p.m.

Sample of the type of question asked:

(a) Why, if the country is so short of money, does not the Mint print more?

(b) If you can get only 90% mortgages from the Building Society why cannot you borrow the other 10% from a Bank?

By this time, you will have recognised our attempts at organising the mathematics studies of the pupil in a way which avoids a static operation carried out on a classroom desk top, but nevertheless we would be the last to deny that the latter position still plays a useful part in the pupil's mathematical education.

The lively responses of our pupils, together with the degree of interest they manifest in their mathematical studies, encourage us in our quest for variety in approach and for taking the limited mathematics of these pupils into their lives and their environment.

We conclude with a brief description of the annual mathematics competition organised on a year basis. A pro forma containing some 25 items is issued to those wishing to compete, and this they take away and return by a specified date when they have filled it in to their satisfaction. We do not think that we delude ourselves when we believe that it is neither for the pleasure of form filling, nor for the joy of the very small prize offered, that this competition maintains its impetus. Rather do we think that it provides us with some evidence that these very ordinary pupils can take this very ordinary mathematics into their lives with pleasure and with considerable enthusiasm.

Here is a fourth year competition form we have used:

FOURTH YEAR MATHEMATICS COMPETITION

Name ....Form...........................

1. What is the weight of a pint of water?
2. What is the time of departure of a train listed at 13.56 hours?
3. How many halfpennies would you have to place side by side to stretch one yard?
4. What is the weight of a house brick?..........lb.
5. What is the approximate length of the front of the school? ....yards
6. What is the average length of a man's tie?..........in.
7. Find the area of the central quad in square feet..........
8. What is the colour of a 6d postage stamp.
9. How many figures are there on the world cup stamps?
10. What is the approximate height of Consfield Castle?
11. What does 8 mean on a wood boring drill?
12. How many days will there be in February next year?
13. What is the thickness of this piece of paper?
14. What is the area of this piece of paper?
15. What is the average height of a chair seat?
16. Find the approximate diameter of an adult size bicycle wheel.
17. How many $\frac{1}{16}$ in. in $5\frac{3}{8}$ in?
18. Find the approximate weight of an egg..........oz.
19. Find the approximate weight of two pennies..........oz.
20. How many steps are there up to Consfield Castle Keep?
21. How many degrees does the minute hand of a clock travel from quarter past to 5 min to the next hour?..........degrees.
22. What is average number of matches in an ordinary match box?
23. How far is it from Consfield to Shefborough?..........miles.
24. What is the average height of a school desk?
25. What are the numbers to be found on the extreme top of a sign post?

Return to Mr. Wood, Room 26, before December 12th.

In this article we have attempted to present a rather condensed picture of the various approaches to mathematics work we adopt in this school. From it you may deduce a little, but only a little of the content of our mathematics courses. For our part, we sense the vigour and stimulation of the work, and although we cannot really speak for the pupils, we believe that they enjoy and are interested in their mathematics. On the strength of this then, we anticipate that no great difficulties will arise when those pupils who are non examinees will stay with us for a fifth year, but this is not to imply that we 'know all the answers'. We hope that our experiences may prove helpful and encouraging to others engaged in the same field.

6

Action in the South West

After teaching physical education for ten years, I came to a secondary modern school offering my services as a teacher mainly interested in mathematics and technical drawing. I found myself in a co-educational secondary modern school, present roll 350 pupils, representing about 70% of the 11+ age group; about $\frac{2}{5}$ of the pupils coming from urban schools and the remainder from rural schools. The school was founded in 1953 and was housed in a new building of that period.

What prompted me seven years ago to reject the 'chalk-and-talk' method of teaching mathematics? I was asked 'as a start' to take first and second years (11 to 12 years) C and D streams mathematics (along with some technical drawing).

The youngsters and I had enjoyed our physical education but in mathematics I sensed a barrier. Many hated the subject, others tolerated it, but none appeared to enjoy the work. I saw them through to the third and fourth years but with no more success; the pupils at 14 years of age appeared to know little more than they had known at 11 years of age. They produced even less. They were not in the main difficult, just indifferent, willing to do simple mechanical arithmetic — but I suspected only to please me and keep the peace.

What had gone wrong? I asked myself were these youngsters incapable of learning? No — they had memorised the current pop songs and a vast amount of knowledge about their idols — they knew by heart all the T.V. commercials, and most of them earned money in a busy seaside town.

It was obvious that I had to try a different approach; to create and stimulate interest in the subject. I had somehow to provide the youngsters with material in which they could actively participate, to make the instructions simple enough for them to understand and so ensure a success motivation; they were conscious of failure in mathematics hitherto.

I made a start with fractions. A number of tomato boxes (3d each) were filled with fraction material — not for me to handle and explain — for *them* to work with and 'discover'.

Work cards were put into each box — until finally there was enough material to begin 'equal parts', halves, thirds, quarters, etc. working through to $\frac{3}{8} + \frac{1}{4} : \frac{1}{8} + \frac{3}{10} : \frac{9}{10} + \frac{4}{5}$ etc. but using as many every day materials as I could possibly think of to 'do' the problems.

51

Here are some examples of the assignments used with these 'boxes'.

CARD 101

Copy this into your book — complete the answers as Fractions.
I looked at a square card
If I were to cut down the red dotted line there would be..........
for you and..........for me.
I looked at a card cut into a circle
There would be..........for you and..........for me.
I looked at a package of TEA containing A POUND
Each of the small packets contained......... of a pound.
The Price of the TEA was..........for a quarter of a pound.
The Price for a pound of TEA was..........

CARD 102

Copy the following into your book — fill in the missing answers.
   1. You will see a ONE PINT milk bottle
   2. Fill a small milk bottle with water and pour into the ONE PINT bottle
   3. It took..........of the small bottles to fill the ONE PINT bottle
   4. Small bottle must contain..........(a fraction) of a PINT
   5. Jack and Mary together use..........(a fraction) of a PINT
   6. If I use a small bottle of milk per day for SIX days I will have used..........pints all together.
   7. If I drink a small bottle of milk each day for EIGHT days I will have used..........pints all together.

CARD 103

Copy this into your book — complete the answers.
I looked at the Standard Block of Wood
It was cut into..........equal parts.
If I gave Jane a piece of wood she would have..........
(a fraction) of the whole.
If I gave pieces of wood to Jane, Jack and John there would be..........(a fraction) of the whole remaining.
I looked at the standard rod of wood
It was cut into..........equal parts
If you took..........(a fraction) there would be..........(a fraction) left for me.

52

Copy this into your book.

The large red rod is a whole unit.

1. What colour are the halves? Ans.
2. What fraction is *one* yellow piece? Ans.
3. Two yellow pieces are..........(a fraction) Ans.
4. What colour is $\frac{1}{6}$?.......... Ans.
5. Empty a slot and put $\frac{1}{3}$ and $\frac{1}{6}$ in the slot
   Now empty the slot at the side of them
   How many light green pieces make the same length as the $\frac{1}{3}$ and $\frac{1}{6}$ added together?.......... Ans.
6. $\frac{1}{3} + \frac{1}{6}$ .... Ans.
7. How many blue pieces will make the same length as questions 5 and 6?
   What is this as a fraction?.......... Ans.
8. How many purple pieces will make this length?.......... Ans.
   What is this as a fraction?.......... Ans.
9. Using the blocks what is $\frac{2}{3} + \frac{1}{6}$?.......... Ans.
10. What is $\frac{1}{2} + \frac{1}{6}$?.......... Ans.

Using the boxes work out the following:

1. $\frac{1}{2} + \frac{1}{4} =$

2. $\frac{1}{4} + \frac{1}{8} =$

3. $\frac{1}{8} - \frac{1}{16} =$

4. $\frac{1}{5} + \frac{1}{10} =$

5. $\frac{1}{6} + \frac{1}{12} =$

6. $\frac{1}{3} + \frac{1}{12} =$

7. $\frac{3}{8} + \frac{1}{16} =$

8. $\frac{3}{5} + \frac{2}{10} =$

9. $\frac{5}{8} + \frac{2}{16} =$

10. $\frac{3}{6} + \frac{3}{12} =$

11. $\frac{3}{10} + \frac{1}{10} =$

12. $\frac{2}{3} + \frac{5}{12} =$

I picked out a couple of pupils at a time to have a go at working through the boxes while the rest of the class proceeded as usual from the black board and/or text books. I was soon inundated by youngsters who wanted to try the boxes. They did not seem to mind that perhaps the work was not relevant to their particular requirements. They were keen to handle the simplest of materials and record their findings whereas similar questions in purely abstract terms had been rejected.

Now here was the challenge! Could I expand and repeat this 'Guided

Discovery Method' over the whole spectrum of mathematics? Seven years later and with over 500 work cards and boxes available to my mathematics streams I am constantly adding to and improving the system, which I feel though in its infancy can claim to be the beginnings of a mathematics workshop.

The organisation of the workshop, probably its most important feature, has evolved through numerous pitfalls. At the outset I realised that the box/card system must be dispersed over a wide area to prevent pupils waiting at one shelf or cupboard for cards and/or materials.

I spread out the cards and boxes in numerical order over every window ledge and shelf in the area.

I keep in front of me a 'MASTER PLAN BOARD' which reads (for example):

	Road	Acc.	Milk	Exports	M.p.h.		
Graphs	105		248	227	238	etc.	
	Bus	Sea	24 hr.	Air	Air	Rail	
Time Tables	107	232	270	164	321	358	etc.
Land Survey	110	111	235	etc.			
Volumes	250	234	50	231	285	etc.	
Bearing/Maps	271	272	345	346	354	356	etc.
%	113	148	43	42	46	etc.	
Ratio & Prop.	288	133	291	58	etc.		

The numbers in the cards and boxes may appear meaningless; but in fact they are all progressively programmed.

The first box or card reading from the Topic title, is the simplest, irrespective of its number and then all cards in that topic increase in difficulty.

This 'loose' number system has the advantage that at any time another card can be slipped in, where a programmed 'step' has been found too difficult.

Each pupil keeps a work/card record at the back of his exercise book which follows him through the years.

A typical page might read:

Date	Card	Signature
October 1967	58, 59, 60	J.H.
July 1967	61, 62	J.H.
November 1967	63, 64	J.H.

In practice when I first get a class from the junior schools, I do some 'diagnostic' testing. From the testing and questioning I am soon able to 'key-in' each child to the system where I think he has most to gain.

54

For example: Question 31 'If your bicycle wheel has a radius of 14 in.,

(a) what is its diameter?

(b) what will its circumference be?'

If this reveals a blank then the pupil will be booked for Box 104 in the future, which contains all the relevant material for 'discovering' the radius/diameter/circumference relationships. It may be that he has had some experience of earliest concepts in, say, ratio/proportion and can begin this further up the ladder, missing out some of the discovery boxes.

Box 104

Borrow a tape measure from Mr. Holmes.
    Copy the following into your book — neatly — and fill in the answers.
1. Measure the diameter of the cycle wheel.
    It measured.......... in.
2. The circumference of the cycle wheel measured.......... in.
3. The diameter of the large metal ring was.......... in.
4. The circumference of the large metal ring was.......... in.
5. The diameter of the small metal ring was.......... in.
6. The circumference of the small metal ring was.......... in.
7. The diameter of the small hardboard card.......... in.
8. The circumference of the small hardboard card.......... in.
9. The diameter of each of these circles fits into its circumference
    .... times.

Many work cards are done as individual assignments, but helpers are enlisted as the task demands.
For example

(a) Height of school; height of cliffs above the beach; width of river estuary; (three pupils). There is a time limit given for this also.

(b) Traffic census (two pupils).

(c) Speed of school Go Kart (four pupils).

Here are some examples of cards used in the context of time and travel.

Take a Western National Bus Time-Table   **CARD 107**

Turn to *Index to Places Served*

Copy the questions — fill in the answers.

    1. What service number is the Newquay-Padstow Service?..........

    2. The Newquay-Padstow Service is on Page..........

    3. What time does the first bus leave Newquay using this service?..........

    4. It does not go as far as Padstow but only as far as..........

    5. How many buses per day make the full journey Newquay to Padstow (without having to change buses)?..........

    6. When the bus leaves Newquay at 10.25, what time does it arrive at Padstow?..........

    7. When the bus leaves Newquay at 16.00 put the 'normal' clock times in brackets) — what time does it arrive in Padstow?..........

    8. How long does the journey take?..........

    9. The last bus of the day to Padstow is at?..........

    10. What is its arrival time? (and 'normal' time)?..........

    Read Page 2 about the 24 hour clock

Using the Airline Time-Table provided.   **CARD 321**

Copy these questions — fill in the answers.

    1. Change these 'normal' times to 24 hour clock times

    (a) 6 p.m.   (b) 4.30 p.m.   (c) 9.20 p.m.   (d) 7.55 p.m.   (e) 9.30 a.m.

    2. Change these to 'normal' clock times

    (a) 14.00 hr   (b) 18.30 hr   (c) 23.45 hr   (d) 07.00 hr (e) 10.20 hr

    3. Find the London-Newquay flights

If you leave London at 15.55 hr what time should you arrive in Newquay?..........

In normal time this is.......... p.m.

    4. If you depart Newquay 11.45 hr what time should you arrive in London?..........

    5. How long does the journey Newquay-London take?..........

    6. If you depart Newquay at 10.45 hr what time should you arrive in Manchester?..........

    7. Why is the time at Newquay Coach Terminal given? (Write a sentence).

    8. Find the distance from Newquay to London.......... miles

Find the distance from Newquay to Manchester.......... miles

    9. What is the cost of flying Newquay-London (Page 23)?..........

    10. What is the cost of travelling by rail Newquay-London?..........

    (Answers on the packet).

Some cards also, which taken together form a 'programme', on the finding of heights and distances.

---

1. Take the three polished blocks of equal heights and line them up on the table – (2 ft apart or so).

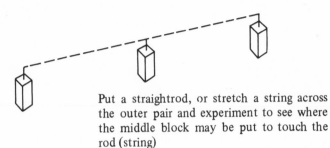

Put a straightrod, or stretch a string across the outer pair and experiment to see where the middle block may be put to touch the rod (string)

2. Take the three blocks of different heights and repeat the experiment. What important difference do you find?

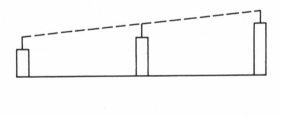

Work with a partner – copy the drawings into your book – put in *all* the sizes marked *x–y–z* etc.
Equipment – Pencil – paper – tape measure – 6 ft pole – 2ft pole
1. Set up in the following manner

Measure *y* ft =
Measure *z* ft =
Calculate *x* ft =

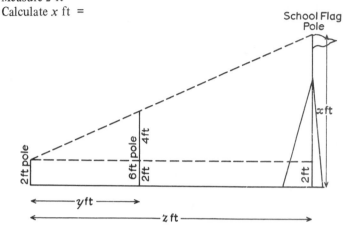

2. Measure *y* ft =
   Measure *z* ft =
   Calculate *x* ft =

1. Set up the posts *flat* on the BOYS' COURT

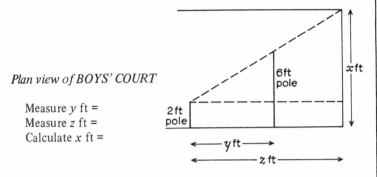

Plan view of BOYS' COURT

Measure y ft =
Measure z ft =
Calculate x ft =

2. Draw this and by mathematics, find the distance across this river.

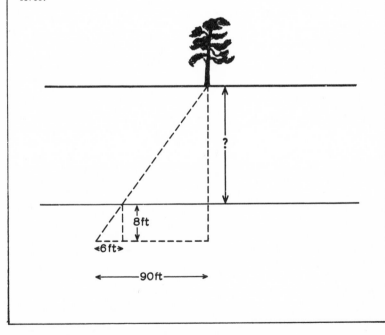

The progression from a simple table top preparatory task to full scale working out of doors is exemplified here.

This type of organisation solves the problem of requiring

    30 or so surveying instruments

    30 or so tape measures

    30 or so ship's compasses

    30 or so desk calculators, etc.

Programmed books, a teaching machine, two slide/film strip projectors are in constant use in the room. Each film strip — each 'clip' of slides and every programmed book is numbered and fits into a topic somehow along the line.

There are occasions when I call a halt and take a class lesson; usually the situation arises from pupils' questions.

For example

1. When decimal currency was mooted.

2. Breathalysers — % of road accidents — figures can be 'bent'.

3. Graphs — can be half truths — topical T.V.

4. T.V. mathematics programmes.

These allow the very useful class participation — discussion and follow-up where necessary.

Typical chatter:

Derek: 'I.T.V. is much better for Sport'.

Colin: 'No it's not, B.B.C. give much more time to Sport'.

Teacher: 'Right boys, bring last week's B.B.C. (Radio Times) and I.T.V. (Look Westward) and draw a graph showing the time allocated to Sport/Drama/Documentaries and Pop Music.' (This immediately becomes a card in the Graphs Topic.)

Correlation or the blurring of subject frontiers occurs naturally and when the situation presents itself.

(a) The Physical Education Department requires a 440 yard athletic track with four lanes and a staggered start. The request is made. Three or four boys survey the field — scale-draw the track. Measure and peg out the track. Once the groundsman is satisfied — he goes over the lanes with marking machine (5th year boys).

(b) A member of the school-band wants to make a Post-horn. The horn is developed in Technical Drawing/Mathematics made in metalwork — played in music lessons (4th year boy).

(c) A Work card on curtaining the windows of the mathematics room relies on the co-operation of Needlework Department (3rd year girls).

(d) Three 4th year girls discovered that the graph on Heights/Weights of school children distributed by the Milk Marketing Board showed a serious discrepancy, when compared with the pupils of our own school. They wrote to the Milk Marketing Board (English) suggesting that:
either,

Children in the South West were much taller and heavier than the national average,
or,
The graphs were years out of date. (The latter proved to be the case).

(e) A mixed team of 14 year olds took a census of people visiting the Royal Cornwall Show (Agriculture). Their figures proved to be of great interest to the organisers. Total sample 700. Agriculture 48.5%, Retired 10.9%, Building Trades 10.0%, Education 4.9%, Public Services 4.3%, Shops distributive 4.3%, Summer visitors 4.0%, Fishing 2.0%, China Clay 2.15%, Hotels catering 1.43%, Doctor Dentists 1.42%, Other 6.1%.

(f) A 14 year old boy, whose father is a village blacksmith/farm implement repairer, asked could he design a corn-hopper and find its cubic capacity. (I learned that corn will only flow on a gradient of +44°.)
He made a drawing of the hopper — made it in card to scale (Technical/Mathematics). Worked out its capacity. (The blacksmith made it for a local farmer and now the school gets lots of favours from the smith!)

(g) Some new class rooms were being added to the school. After a word with the Surveyors, four boys checked up the land and levels. Along with other stints of work they calculated the amount of ready-mix concrete necessary for the foundations. The boys said 6 cu yards would be sufficient — the foremen had ordered 9 cu yards. (3 cu yards were eventually returned to the Ready-Mix company.)

(h) Three boys made a Go Kart in metalwork. They marked out a track on the tarmac area using ex-hose pipes. One lap was made to be 110 yards. The Go Kart was timed for four laps. The speed in miles per hour and the fuel consumption in miles per gallon were calculated.

(i) The school sailing club has three boats (self-made) and we are able to make navigation meaningful to most.
A mock up boat has been made for class room use, large enough for a pupil to sit in and read a genuine ship's compass on the bridge.
Typical question: 'You are leaving the local harbour and sailing due north. Plot a course for Dublin on the chart provided and set the ship on course.' (Ask teacher to check this.)

Further, take a compass bearing of Trevose Head and Towan Head and show your position on the map provided. (Ask teacher to check this.)

These maps and charts are run off in Technical Drawing using a dyeline process. A typical work card in this section is Card 356.

CARD 356

Take map 356 (British Isles)
Use a protractor and find the following bearings:

1. Newquay	–	New York	=	.... °
2. Newquay	–	Dublin	=	.... °
3. Southampton	–	Barbados	=	....
4. Dover	–	Calais	=	....
5. Harwich	–	Esberg	=	....
6. Newcastle	–	Oslo (a)	=	....
		(b)	=	....

Two Readings
Set the 'Boat' on course – ask teacher to check the following:
(a) Turn the boat so that it is on course Newquay – New York.
(b) Turn the boat so it is on course Newquay – Dublin.
(c) Set the boat on a course Newcastle – Bergen.

This approach is not designed to make life easy for the teacher – it is very demanding, and its critics will insist that it is uneconomic to teach every process 30 (or more) times.

To the last named I would say that I now realise that I probably 'over-talked' when black board teaching. Children will grasp many things – graphs spring to mind – with the minimum of instructions. How demanding? As each child comes to my desk, I look up the last assignment; enter it on the record card and make a quick decision on what to set next. I then do some teaching until I feel the child is ready to proceed alone.

If, while teaching, a queue begins to form, I resort to giving those waiting a repetition card – one very similar to the card just concluded.

At this stage it would be presumptuous to claim outstanding 'success' with pupils using this method, but if concentration, enjoyment and satisfaction are criteria then there is a large measure of success.

Pupils' quotes:

14 year old boy: 'With a teacher working from a black board – I am always waiting for him to finish, with this method you can just get on with the cards.'

12 year old boy: 'It's nice – always different and something new to do. My father likes me to talk about it.'

13 year old girl: 'I enjoy it, working from cards, but sometimes it's better to learn from the black board where teacher has more time.'

13 year old boy: 'It doesn't seem to be mathematics at all — I like it especially the machines.'

(2 Projectors, 1 Auto Tutor Teaching Machine, 1 Desk Calculator are 'keyed' into the system.)

Conclusion

The approach to mathematics learning which I first introduced some seven years ago, is only possible with the full support of the Headmaster and my colleagues within the school: this I have had in full measure. Some may think that I was fortunate in having a room which could be adapted solely for the purpose: while seven years ago there may have been some substance in this contention, at the present time, such a provision can be regarded as minimal for the learning of mathematics with 'things', rather than with symbols alone. Again, the provision of such visual aids as we use, of programmed texts and the like, has been a matter not for the mathematics department alone, but as part of a wider school development policy. Whilst grateful for the goodwill and support afforded me within the school, I am very conscious of a sense of isolation, in that such ideas as I have developed have been translated into action in a relatively rural area.

I would make no claim to having solved all the problems inherent in this kind of approach; rather have I just made a beginning and must continue the process of trial and error in order to progress. The main questions which require continued attention are:

(1) Ensuring a sequential development of mathematical content.

(2) Finding and maintaining the delicate balance between the time devoted to individual work and the time devoted to group/class teaching.

If I can find more satisfactory answers to these questions, then the organisational details of materials to meet the needs will fall into a proper perspective.

As previously stated, I can confidently claim a vast improvement in the attitude shown by the pupils who learn their mathematics by this approach. As I see it, the *quality* of their learning has improved at the expense of the *quantity* previously attempted by normal class teaching methods. Daily evidence of the sense of satisfaction found by the pupils with this approach together with my own inner sense of satisfaction, with our progress are the chief rewards for the time I spend in preparing and organising this 'Workshop' approach to mathematics learning.

63

7

Mathematics for Fourth Year Leavers

Josephine Mold, Abbey Wood School

Inspired by Mr. Owen's account of his work with boys (Mathematics Teaching No. 23) I have put together some thoughts on my work this year (1963-64) with a class of 4th year girls. They followed a one year 'Social Education' course; the other options for girls being academic and commercial courses.

Four main difficulties quickly became apparent. The most acute was the wide ability range in the class. The girls were drawn from streams 3 to 7 in a 7 class comprehensive entry year. Thus a few had the ability to follow an academic course leading to G.C.E., although they had chosen not to, and some had difficulty in reading anything but the simplest material.

The second problem was one of size. There were over 30 on roll. This is common, I know, but nevertheless it is far too many for comfort in this type of class, made up as it was of girls who seemed to need plenty of personal attention. Unfortunately (or perhaps fortunately for me) the attendance problem was such that there were seldom more than 25 at school on any one day and frequently, by Friday, we were down to a manageable 20. If only it were always the same 20 and not a selection of the $^{32}C_{20}$ combinations!

Another big problem was purely a social one. Most of the 'problem children' in the year wanted to leave at the earliest opportunity and thus we found them almost all in this class, whereas before, their differing intelligence had kept them apart from one another. As a result certain behaviour and anti-social difficulties began to emerge at first and may have affected girls who had not come into contact with them before. Happily there was a definite maturing during the year and, by the second term, quite an adult and responsible atmosphere had begun to build up. I sincerely hope that this was in part due to the attitude of self-organisation and self-reliance that their teachers were trying to instil.

The last of the major problems was 'motivation'. This we know is bound up with the level and content of the work, the outlook of the class, the attitude at home and the personality of the teacher.

It seems to me that there are three basically different ways of working with a class such as this. I employ all three of them depending on the other factors involved. They are, firstly, teaching the class as a whole; secondly,

64

group work on different topics; and thirdly, entirely individual work based, perhaps, on topic cards.

The first method, that of class teaching, has a very obvious disadvantage for a mixed ability group. For this reason I use it very seldom. It is most effective if I am dealing with some subject matter which is new to everyone and in which the ideas are simple enough for the weakest but of interest to the brightest. A tall order, but these topics do occur from time to time. For example, a couple of the girls had interviews for jobs concerned with punched card machines and asked me if I could tell them anything about them. This was the perfect opportunity for a few lessons on punched cards, computer tape, the binary system, the number cards necessary to hold 1, 2, 3 ... n pieces of information, etc. They were particularly interested in decoding punched tape and putting shuffled binary punched cards in order. I think they were all keen on this piece of work and it left one or two interesting leads which could be followed up by individuals later.

Another joint effort was the collection and study of competitions especially the put-in-order type or the matching-pairs type. They worked out the number of ways each could be done (and how much it would cost you to be sure of a winning line) and this led on to some elementary work on chance and choice. We also worked together, at least in the initial stages, on tessellations of regular and irregular plane shapes, developing a particular interest in interlocking patterns. This topic, of course, left many paths open for follow up later at various levels.

The group work method seems fraught with difficulties if the groups have more than two members. The weaker or lazier ones tend to leave the work to the others and it is always the absentee who has all the vital information for the day's work! Some of the girls still found it difficult to co-operate with someone else for any length of time. However, I still use this method often, because I feel most strongly that we must show them how to work on a job with others. An improvement in their ability to do this was noticeable during the year.

Group work seemed to be the best way of tackling statistical surveys. The girls study the likes, dislikes, ambitions, etc. of various year-groups and compiled frequency graphs leading to normal and non-normal distributions. I believe that the most socially useful piece of work which they undertook was an investigation into school attendance. Using the registers they studied the correlation between the attendance and academic grouping in the 4th year and also between the day of the week and the number of absentees, taking the figures over the entire previous year. They were really shocked that their own attendance was so much worse than the corresponding boys' class and the academic, technical and commercial courses. I think that they had not really believed us before when we said that Friday afternoon was the worst of the week. This turned out to be a very valuable piece of work and provoked a lot of discussion, particularly about payment of sick benefit by employers and by the State.

Individual project work is the method I have found most useful with this class but it can only work if you are prepared to cope with up to 30 different things at once and if your colleagues are as tolerant of activity as mine are. I use a series of about 40 work cards as 'starters'. These are constantly added to, changed, or thrown out. This system has big advantages in that work can be provided at different levels, it is possible to stimulate interest by variety, and everyone tends to produce their own efforts if only because no one else will do two different lots to help them out. I often find that ideas are followed up which have not been on a card but which have occurred while working on something else.

The cards are only intended as pointers. Many of them have appropriate pictures stuck on them and each has a few lines of introduction, references to suitable books, and perhaps one or two ideas for making or doing. The books to which I refer might be from my own collection, from the department or school library or may even be one of the few class books which have made any attempt to cater for the 4th year leaver. They have a tendency to consist of disguised exercises and neither encourage nor suggest further reading, enquiry or activity. Project books, which would not spoon feed, but which would lead the pupil into mathematical activity in a wider sense rather than to arithmetical exercises or the mere copying of geometrical designs, would be ideal for this class.

What criteria can we use for choosing topics? At this stage I think that the main one must be interest, although I have become very wary of passing judgement on this myself. For example, I think that accounts are dull, but I discovered that the girls wanted very much to do some 'book-keeping', a high prestige subject in their minds, and so we did a bit of that. In no way do I press arithmetic on them but any cards dealing with household and commercial arithmetic seem very popular because many of them feel that they must be able to see a clear application in their work. Other topics from the cards include statistics, mathematical models and drawings, travelling, graphs and diagrams, astronomy, etc. There is very often an overlap from one subject to another and each card has a number 1, 2 or 3 on it to indicate a broad standard. The tendency to choose one which is too easy is counteracted by the fact that the harder ones are usually more interesting for the more able girl. I often found that someone would start at card 1 of a topic and work up to 3 in that section rather than do another subject at the first level. It is not necessary to stick to the card at all: I intend them only as a stimulus, other stimuli comes from seeing what others in the class are doing and from discussions, ideas or events.

I found (somewhat to my surprise) that, after an initial settling in period, my presence was almost superfluous. I spent the lessons wandering around the room with a bit of advice here and there and perhaps a short discussion with one or two girls. I had some surprises from time to time. One of the duller girls got very involved in some statistical calculations on the borrowing rate from the school library. I introduced her to logarithms which she used with great enthusiasm and success. Another, seemingly little interested, began to study household expenses and went round the local shops one weekend listing the prices of all she might need in a week. She suddenly produced this after school one day and we had a most useful discussion on the problems involved, not all mathematical!

Various other topics created general interest during the year. A representative of the local National Savings Committee came to talk during one maths. lesson and there followed brisk activity about interest, methods of saving, pocket money, endowments, insurance, H.P. versus cash, banks, cheques, etc. I am quite sure that had I just started a normal classroom course on this, I would not have got the response which came because they decided to follow up the talk.

In the final term a group wanted to build a scale model of the school — by this time our maths. lessons had been cut to three a week to make room for other activities (I was delighted at their disappointment over this) so the model was never finished. However the work that was done provided an object lesson for that group in organisation and common sense as well as elementary surveying and measurement.

At Easter half the class left and the number on the roll seemed quite ideal. It was big enough for variety but small enough for discussion as a group. News seeped in from the leavers. Discussions on wages, national insurance, income tax, fares, budgets, etc. arose spontaneously from this.

Another constant source of interest was the activities of younger children. We dipped into multi-base arithmetic, movement geometry, binary adders, correlations of height and weight, distribution curves, coin tossing and probability to keep up with young brothers and sisters. From their pinnacle of sophistication they looked at Cuisenaire rods and other concrete material. After all in a few years they will be the mothers of children who are doing all this 'new-fangled maths.'

What about next year? I've already made a few promises to 3rd year girls who have come to ask what we shall do! I'll throw away at least half the cards; I'll continue to run my class as a sort of mathematical 'social club', I'll beg, borrow or steal some 'proper paper' in case they want to do bookkeeping and I'll get, I hope, some new ideas from readers of Mathematics Teaching . . . please.

8

Autobiography of a Mathematics Teacher

It began with a class of retarded nine year olds where reading and writing were even greater problems to me than number. In desperation I visited an Infant School — and so began communication. The ice having been broken, the interchange of ideas became fruitful in many fields. The changes in my own attitude and approaches resulted in a changed appearance of our classroom. Changes in procedure following the introduction of equipment were startling, and an apparent increase in some children's ability puzzled the Headmaster, although *I* believed that the reintroduction of what one might the have termed 'infant' methods revealed the natural ability of such pupils.

My new outlook affected the fourth year juniors too and we established real contact with our neighbouring secondary modern schools. I had taught in the senior department of an 'all through' school, but great educational changes had taken place, although only just beginning in mathematics, in the fifteen years since the inception of the secondary modern schools. More communication — more discussions, visits to other schools — revealed the possibility of success and enjoyment of mathematics for the ordinary secondary child. I had always enjoyed mathematics myself, but teaching it was a chore — now suddenly I felt that there was some hope.

I undertook a One Year Supplementary Course in Mathematics for secondary teachers at a College of Education. Looking back now I see that year as one of mental endeavour, rather than physical experience; a period of germination of creative ideas rather than a time of finding solutions. I realised that in the early days, the secondary modern school was unique in having no examinations. With the raising of the school leaving age time had been ripe for a reshaping of mathematics syllabus to offer a planned four year course. Arithmetic alone gave place to mathematics — ideally more integrated than the arithmetic, algebra, geometry of the grammar schools. What is more, the opportunity to break with the traditional syllabus, its order content and presentation was there for those who believed that a watered down grammar school syllabus was not necessarily the best for all pupils. The day of the practical situation emerged and even although many of the approaches popular then are considered old-fashioned now, their advent opened teachers' minds to the *ongoing* need for new light and new visions. I was particularly intrigued by work in geometry — formerly the bête noir of so many teachers and pupils, and it seemed so easy to see where it had been going wrong.

'Mathematical justice for the less able . . . demands a new outlook and great skills from the teachers' said a Ministry Pamphlet of the time (Teaching Mathematics in Secondary Schools. Pamphlet 36 (HMSO)). The implication was that mathematics had never been taught successfully to any but the able and there had never been any conscious need to consider the mysteries of its peculiar learning difficulties. We learnt that research was going on and that we must keep abreast of development through reading and through communication with colleagues, with the school down the road, through the professional organisations.

We were involved, as pupils, in practical work. Although we had not experienced this method of teaching we saw that the teacher needed a quick appreciation of the situation when pupils encountered unforeseen difficulties and needed to guard against giving too much guidance when the pupil is working on material very familiar to the teacher. Our own rôle of pupils taught us much about the rôle of the teacher. In particular two principles emerged; one was understanding of the difference between a mathematical concept and the calculations or operations based on that concept; the other was the belief that for many children mathematical concepts are best acquired through practical situations.

By the time my one year course ended even more secondary schools were welcoming teachers who were willing to experiment in teaching mathematics to ordinary children. My first year of experiment with the lower streams of the notorious 3rd year secondary was spectacular; maps and drawings, charts and graphs, curve stitchings and artistic projects on the circles, parabola, spiral were much in evidence, together with some history of their discovery. We measured heights of local landmarks, surveyed the grounds, studied projections and plans and visited the Weights and Measures Office. Above all the mathematics however, the greatest value seemed to be the personal relationships which developed between pupils and teachers and the overspill of enthusiasm into other areas of the curriculum.

My Head of Department appeared keen on this kind of work. The official syllabus had a new look and new textbooks and apparatus were available. The 1st and 2nd year pupils followed a more restrained programme geared to the 13+ selection test, and with those pupils I was not often allowed to follow the practical approach. The policy for using the new textbooks followed the line of 'throw the book at them in the first year'. There were plenty of insertions of new material but little integration; making what seemed a bewildering medley. Everyone, however, was purposefully engaged and there was opportunity for group and individual work.

In the Upper School I moved towards topics in an effort to achieve integration. Some grew to grand proportions. For example the end product of some simple work on a shadow stick was a huge graph showing hours of daylight over a whole year. Times of sunrise and sunset led to some intricate scale calculations and spilt over into the geography lesson.

My stay was too short to see long term development, but the pupils showed me how this way of working could encourage spontaneity and life in the classroom, and I realized the problems which restraints such as the 13+ examination created in the working of a school.

A Senior post in another school enabled me once again to develop the topic approach with the average pupils. No new books or apparatus were available this time, but the opportunity to plan an integrated course from the start presented itself. With one class I worked from E. J. James's topic books (Published by Oxford) on *The Aircraft Pilot* following on to *Aircraft Navigation*. This topic involved measures of force, ratios, decimals, graphs, directed numbers, scale plans, temperature, instrument readings, speeds, mach numbers, timetables, scale, bearings, magnetic variation and wind vectors. The work was recorded in loose leaf files together with relevant supporting material from newspapers and magazines. I felt the work with these groups was worthwhile and achieved something in the all-round development of my pupils, but it was not without its worrying cross currents. There was considerable pressure from parents and hence fierce competition for a place in the 'A' stream to sit for the County Certificate Examinations. This resulted in frequent examinations for 'A' stream pupils, to maintain their entitlement, and hence in a floating group in the 'A' stream, subjected to the tensions and anxieties of keeping up, catching up in time or worse still being relegated to the 'B' stream where all was lost. Sometimes those relegated regained confidence under a new approach and went up again to do well enough in the examination. Sometimes, however, they quickly lost heart and found themselves with us again. One boy moved up and down three times in this way. Even for those making steady and uninterrupted progress, there was the tyranny of a common paper set by the Head of Department for all streams in the year and this paper gave no scope at all for the sort of work my pupils had come to look for and enjoy.

In this school all classes normally had a change of subject teacher each year. This system may have merits, but I felt it produced lack of continuity and the need for pupils to adjust repeatedly to new patterns of teaching and learning. Neither did any member of staff experience the development of the whole syllabus. I was given the opportunity, however, to take one group through from the second year to the fourth year County Certificate Examination and I was encouraged that many of them chose to take mathematics and a number got commendable results; thus strengthening the convictions I had when I began the project.

I could see the all-round development of pupils while I used the topic method, but the disadvantage lay, for me, in the general lack of mathematical unity. An integration of mathematics was limited, for in topics which held real interest pupils did not want to spend time 'discovering' the concepts they needed and flow was interrupted whilst a specific point was taught. Topics have their beginnings and endings, and then what? There is seldom a natural flow between topics and certainly no easy movement between streams in the school. Success can be attributed to the luck of choosing the right topics, others were tried with less success. What topics are successful? The concept of 'child-centred' is left very much to one's own interpretation and new textbooks purporting to relate the material to children's interests mean what adults *think* are children's interests. My course suggested that teachers should pick up topical events and situations from the immediate environment but these can be so done to death in other subjects that perhaps the mathematics lesson offers the only avenue of escape!

I wanted to break away from the textbook and the environment – not to abandon them altogether but to use them as sources of guidance only. I felt, therefore, that there was a need for a unified course for *all* pupils. The idea was beginning to take root that, if one could plan a five year course free of the deterrents of standardizing examinations but with channels of communication between all streams at all times, then perhaps at the end of five years many more students would feel able to seek a qualification in Mathematics and the overall scheme might even be productive in terms of ideas for the very least able. I wanted a course in which we could have complete integration and yet retain individual expression and the power of discovery.

Quite suddenly my channels of communication guided me to the main stream of a similar enquiry. We were visited by a newly appointed County Inspector of Mathematics. His tremendous enthusiasm inspired lively discussion on the syllabus, method, choice and use of texts, and a hundred and one other matters all with an interwoven theme of *growth in mathematics*. By his words and his subsequent exciting demonstration lesson he pinpointed the theme I was looking for – *growth and movement discernible in pattern*.

At this time there was talk about the nature and purpose of the proposed C.S.E. examination and there was mounting evidence of activity with new schemes and syllabuses of the type envisaged in the Report of the Organisation for Economic Co-operation and Development (O.E.C.D.) *Synopsis for modern secondary school mathematics*. More reading, enquiry and County Day Conferences opened up a promising new world with ample material and opportunity for setting up just those conditions I had hoped for in matters of content and type of examination.

In the summer of 1963 I became Head of Mathematics in a 4-stream entry secondary modern school. I received details of a project whose experimental syllabus was in its first year of trial; but the material was too grammar school biased for me. I was looking for new syllabus content which illustrated my theme of growth and movement and which was powerful enough to compel reorientation of teaching methods. At the same time I wanted the material to present a personal challenge and to offer opportunity for experiment which might lead towards revealing the learning patterns particular to the lower streams. At this point I attended a conference about the Midlands Mathematics Experiment. The following extracts from the M.M.E. Report 1962/3 particularly impressed me:

'The only worthwhile way of tackling the problem was not by amending, modifying or manoeuvering existing courses, but to start afresh from Form 1, with a "blank cheque", developing ideas as they seem to fit and be relevant to the aims of the type of programme envisaged in the O.E.C.D. Reports'. . . .

'Mathematics must grow; it must not come to a dead end . . . we are continually being surprised by what children *can* do provided that it grows out of their own peculiar experiences'.

'This is a syllabus for general education and not for mathematics specialists; above all it is in teaching techniques that there must be the greatest change.'

I was introduced to a teacher whose school, a secondary modern, was taking part in the M.M.E. and I later visited his school with my Headmistress. My observation of a 4th stream class in action and of the work of other classes confirmed that the work of this experiment was suitable for secondary modern pupils. We decided to join the M.M.E., which was in any case organised right on our own doorstep and accordingly we became a second-phase entry school.

One of the most valuable products of the experiment was the opportunity for frequent local meetings to further our own mathematical knowledge and to interchange ideas for presentation — this was particularly useful for teachers like myself who were the only maths specialists at their respective schools.

I decided that all four of the new 1st year streams would take part in the experiment together with the top 2nd year stream. For the B, C and D streams in the 2nd year we would try to develop our own experimental syllabus over a period of time. I was expecting the department to grow to three full-fime specialists and I planned for one teacher to take all of one year's intake and follow the course through with that year group. This would give the teachers the chance to learn new work gradually, to compensate later for any gaps, and to give everyone experience of using the same material with all levels of ability. I also hoped that the opportunity to take pupils through to the end of the course would be an incentive to teachers to stay with us.

In the summer term before we began the new syllabus I was able to prepare a special 'maths room'. It was a ground floor room with direct access to the playing fields for outdoor work. I arranged the desks in a curved 'conference' formation. There were also some large tables and stools along the back and side of the room. Easily available were supplies of plain, lined, squared and coloured paper and card of various sizes (as at my last school, I intended that work should be done in loose leaf files rather than in exercise books). Around the room were books, pieces of apparatus, magazines and puzzles. The stockroom included knotted ropes, meccano, wooden cubes, pegboard and pegs, metal tubing and other items built up over the the years. The room had a plumb line which could be used as a pendulum, attached to the ceiling, and a large demonstration slide rule and a good supply of crayons, felt pens, and other necessary materials.

I found that I had to do very much more than arrange practical situations for the discovery of specific facts or processes. In the beginning that had been my greatest concern, since a continuous flow of original ideas had never been my strongpoint and it had been a matter of great relief, when in practice, I found that the boys and girls themselves, once started, found their own ways of moving forward and creating new situations which demanded from them decision, critical judgement and intelligent appraisal − I might have pondered for many an hour, on how to contrive these self same effects and achieved nothing but that artificiality, the end results of which are our most dreaded enemies − waning interest and final apathy. Despite this, however, I had never quite lost the fear that ideas might run out, especially perhaps with the younger pupils. Now I must find my starting point from the pupils' own interests and experiences which I must first discover from their activities and explorations in a more or less open situation, and then channel them in a purposeful direction. I dearly wished for instructions, for techniques, for I was as much a novice in this as the children were. It was imperative for the teacher too to explore the situations the pupils would meet to get the feel of the material and to be aware of interesting side-tracks. Yet again there were no printed answers in the draft textbooks. In the initial stages it was a discovery situation for the teacher as well as the pupil.

The vitality of our work owed much to the interplay and communication between streams, but each stream developed extremely individual characteristics. The 1st stream were caught up in the interest of the mathematics itself and the 3rd thought it was 'fun'; the 2nd stream was always very concerned with the writing up − fimly convinced, like many adults, that to be busy is to be successful. Perhaps this was due to an oversight on our part for we had always thought that the 2nd stream stood to receive the better teaching since the snags occurring with the 1st stream, always a little ahead, had often been ironed out − perhaps together with some of the joy of discovery.

The 3rd stream were always full of questions. Why is it that shape? Why is there a gap? Why do we start division at the opposite end to the other sums − and they answered their own questions by their subsequent investigations. This stream offered me the most guidance; their remarks revealed the mental blockages of themselves and others; their questions opened up new developments and their constant watch for pattern alerted me, not so much to the importance of the pattern itself but to the real need that they have to 'connect things up' — to find co-ordination in the world to which they are reaching out.

The interests and experiences of the 4th stream were sparse. The aim first of all was to get them to communicate. Could one go right back to the beginning and use very simple structural materials? Would simple table patterns help them? I took my courage in both hands and started with the first part of L. G. Sealey's *Creative Use of Mathematics in the Primary School* (Blackwell). They enjoyed the table patterns and, although it did not help their memories, it liberated them and we gradually launched into the kind of work the rest of the classes were doing, but slowly and always of a very practical nature so that the end point was reached within two working periods with a homework in between. Absenteeism played havoc with continuity in these lower ability classes. By the end of the third year they were as competent and capable, within their own compass of work, as were the other streams, although they were more adventurous and lively by then than the 2nd stream had ever been. They were a small class and by their fourth year I had enough desk calculators to be able to take them as a class, which I did almost exactly as described in Working Paper 14 p. 40. The aim, of course, is to turn the handle as few times as possible and in working this out, the associative, commutative and distributive laws became truly operational. The pupils had come across them from time to time in various aspects but they now discovered their true significance. They finally laid the ghost of 'Add a nought to multiply by ten' — there were so many noughts already on the machine that it was obvious one did not want any more, besides, there was no place to 'add it'. But they still did not really understand by what magic the unit was transferred to the ten's place — because I had made the mistake of showing them how to multiply by ten with no turns of the handle. I suppose that 'no turns' mysteriously represented the nought. 'All right' I said, seeing their uncertainty, 'register a unit three and turn the handle ten times'. I should have been shockproof by now, but I was dumbfounded at hearing, 'Stop a minute, go slowly, look, ALL the numbers come, in turn. There's the one in the ten's place, now the twenties 'till it gets to thirty. It's like slow motion, isn't it, Miss?' 'You can see just how it happens'. 'I didn't think it was a *different* three'. No comment is needed.

I have written at length concerning this stream because teaching them was an experience and an experiment in itself. The great thing is, I believe, to make a bold decision at the beginning, 'No dithering on the brink, take a deep, determined plunge and never look back.' It is the stage of learning that the secondary school is *supposed* to represent, that causes one to doubt. Were it the infant or primary stage there would be no hesitation and without the apparatus which is so badly needed for this stage of learning the task appears almost impossible.

I am left with two questions. Can this 'backwardness', become a thing of the past through the 'continuous-involvement-of-the-child' approaches, inherent in Nuffield Mathematics and the Primary School integrated-day? Will we be ready when these changes come to the secondary school?

This work began as part of M.M.E., but in the course of time many modifications and changes were introduced, such changes resulting mainly from the reactions of the pupils to the work. I express my gratitude to M.M.E. for getting me started, but my line of thought and action can be traced even further back in time to the O.E.C.D. report as this concluding tabulation will indicate in broad terms.

My line of action	*O.E.C.D. recommendations*
To distinguish clearly between a mathematical concept and the calculation based on that concept.	To emphasise the properties of operations rather than the calculations.
To experiment with sets of numbers — recommended especially for beginning of term revision i.e. something different and yet based in the already familiar.	To experiment with sets of numbers and experiment with the laws of operations — take a new look at them and see the 'mental arithmetic' rules.
Child-centred mathematics, related to life. A knowledge of mathematical concepts can only arise from some practical situation. Child discovers concepts by experimenting rather than theorem learning.	Learning arises from the child's own peculiar experiences. Hence, based in the familiar and related to child's own interests. Child discovers concepts. Open-ended practical situations right from the start.
Suggested that pattern in number is mental and should be made visual through tabulation and graph.	Pattern *is* visual and leads to concepts of relations and functions.
Much teaching through infiltration — absorbing ideas through usage, well before formal treatment. Integration of various branches of mathematics through Topics.	Elementary Set Theory to be the unifying element.
Geometry 'Egyptian thinking' a discovery of space and the relationships we find in it. Geometrical truths discovered through practical methods, observation and paper folding rather than formal mensuration and drawing.	Symmetry, Parallels, Polygons as opposite. Vector Geometry developed through 'navigation'.

Algebra — a form of language observing relationships and expressing them stating the mathematical content of a situation. Developed through 'think of a number' techniques. (Further development in techniques, of factorising, etc., felt to be unnecessary for these pupils.)

Same concepts as opposite. Starting much earlier. A shorthand for what we have discovered, developed to Vector Algebra by time needed.

Let us at least have the breadth of outlook which not only insists on a constant awareness of current educational research but consistently seeks the aid of such scientifically empowered thought. If at the level of the classroom, we lack day to day inspiration, there is encouragement in the thought that the new outlook has to be *met* before it can be introduced; and that is where friends, colleagues, keeping abreast of developments, wide reading, the school down the road, and membership of a professional organisation all come in.

9

Removing Subject Boundaries with Fourth Year Leavers

Lucy M. Witherspoon, George Salter Secondary
Modern Girls' School, West Bromwich

For many years teachers have been experimenting with methods of teaching which it was thought would prove more successful with our slower pupils than the usual academic approach, but much of this work has proved unfruitful because we have assumed that the subject matter of education is sacrosanct. This subject matter is determined by the original academic intentions of education and lends itself to an analytic approach. Indeed, one might suspect that all our subject matter has been selected simply because it lends itself to this particular analytic and logical approach, i.e. analysis, classification, the separation of ideas from reality, the application of these ideas to hypothetical situations.

This is one way of becoming educated. The progress mankind has made on this basis is enormous, but we are all aware that it is an approach which is very foreign to at least 75% of our population and that this proportion fails to progress beyond a very low level of academic analysis. A good memory, a strong ambition and individual attention will force another 10% perhaps, into achieving some success in these fields but we are not tapping the full potential of at least 60% of our children because the subject matter and method has no corresponding mental structure into which it can be fitted and recalled naturally, as part of one's everyday life.

The third year in secondary schools also sees a great change in the attitude of children to their schooling. Adolescence plays an important part in this change but I would like to suggest that the energy released explodes against the mental, emotional and physical restrictions of school simply because they are now restrictions and no longer vehicles of further personal development, as they have been in the junior and lower secondary schools. And this, I am convinced, is so because the academic framework demands a greater refinement of abstraction at a moment when the children's natural development demands a wider range of direct experience. This experience is to be found among people: it deals with personal relationships, it finds expression in social contacts and self discovery, and finally it is as clearly and obviously necessary to each child's development as is reading, writing and number to the infant and junior child. These basic skills are taught in good infant and junior schools

77

by methods which enable each child to feel he is directly in contact with his world and becoming its master. Children in the secondary stage need a similar exploration and growing understanding of the world of people and a growing mastery of themselves within that world.

To deal with this world by means of academic procedures and techniques is easy enough — civics, social studies, modern history, economic geography, vocational opportunities can be analysed, programmed and fed to the children in carefully prepared and measured doses. But this is not the living world to which our children belong. They are being plunged into the analysis of situations which they have not yet explored, of which they have only the vaguest and most unsatisfactory experience and therefore upon which their imaginations cannot work. The experience of being accepted as responsible people and mixing with adults, of carrying responsibility for themselves, of discussing adult problems, of consulting experts on the organisation of our adult world, is the basic material of social education in the same way as experience of number relationships is the basic material of mathematical education. This practical approach to education in social skills and social responsibilities has already proved very successful in ending the feeling of frustration experienced by adolescents faced with more 'academic' work.

We have, therefore, changed the whole system of school organisation for fourth year pupils and we shall change it for the third year also when it is possible to do so. The change involves removing the limitations inherent in a formal timetable and the demarcations imposed by 'subjects'. Six out of ten sessions each week are blank in the sense that no subjects appear on the timetable at all. This time is time to organise things, to create things, to find out, judge and report on things. These 'things' are all connected with the pupils' own lives either at a personal level, or as influences acting upon them through the community or through mass media.

Generally the method is to plunge the children into situations which provide the practical experience of various social skills, not without guidance, but with the situation sufficiently alive, real and open-ended to engage the children in direct personal experience, and allow them opportunities to play their own part in it, preferably so that they can see the results of the part they have played.

'Guidance' takes the form of discussion, collecting information, searching for alternatives and listening to advice before making finally, personal decisions upon which they must act. It involves the give and take of listening to other people's opinions, accepting, as well as giving judgments, working together and smoothing out differences so that action can be taken which will satisfy the working group. It includes discussion of their own reactions to various suggestions in order to recognise and face up to the personal factors which govern their behaviour. It includes a great deal of discussion about their activities in which advice from the pupils themselves is considered by the group and incorporated whenever it proves useful. There is much individual involvement at every stage, for, as in real life, advice may be ignored, and so acceptance itself becomes an active rather than a passive thing. Rejection of advice produces so tremendous an upsurge of determination to prove oneself right, that one very often is right.

The emphasis all the time is on direct experience; gathering it, thinking about it, discussing it with others, recording it. Most of the situations are found outside schools. From this practical experience of social situations, wider problems can be tackled and more imaginative experiences explored through literature, drama, through art and music for those who can participate in these experiences creatively, through social problems appearing in the press, through television news and features, through film documentaries and stories.

Method and material of the course is inextricably bound together and I shall attempt to give details of techniques of teaching and learning while dealing with the subject matter covered in the course.

Basic Skills

The basic practice of mechanical arithmetic is removed from the course and in time might well be cut out altogether. But the application of mathematical skills is used in all sorts of ways in connection with the interest followed by different groups. Accounts are kept of all money spent as a normal part of each child's record. We have had no mistakes made over the spending of their own or school money. Having made an estimate of their needs, in detail, they are given that amount, do their shopping, bring back receipts, write out a statement, attach statements and receipts and hand them in with the change to the member of staff in charge. If they underestimated they use their own money and have it refunded. We use the school fund as our bank, get as much back as we can from the Education Office, and bear the rest ourselves. When our funds run low the pupils organise all sorts of efforts, keep their accounts, hand in their profits and have it announced to the school. Accounts of these efforts are put up on the school notice boards so that everyone is fully informed. Graphs are used for recording results. Working to scale is used for finding distances in connection with their visits. Their enquiries into methods of saving involve considerable work with simple and compound interest. Their comparisons of prices explore Hire Purchase, deferred payments, 'Accounts' at shops, as well as the vagaries of private shops and supermarkets. Bus and train timetables are needed for their excursions and so on. None of this arithmetic is done as such. It is merely part of the 'real life' situation they are exploring at the moment. And each small group (often composed of only two children) may well be doing something quite different.

The practice of English is an integral part of the whole course. 'We learn our native language by learning how to behave in situations, not by learning rules about what to say'. All formal exercises are cut out. All aspects of English work are covered by the discussion, searching for information, recording their work and talking to people and on behalf of people. Only literature, the study of a book, play or poetry is given a timetabled period and a separate existence. This is done largely to ensure the availability of television plays and the help of an expert. It does not require this separation from the main course.

The time devoted to literature is a very specific and important core or heart through which sympathetic understanding of other people and a deeper understanding of themselves develop. These understandings enrich and carry nourishment to the practical work of dealing with people and with themselves.

Thus it is necessary to widen enormously the range of books read, films seen, art looked at; to be adventurous in exploration and to use every means available to keep the children's emotions alive and to provide means of developing both vitality and control. All the great needs of mankind appear in play, story, and novel over and over again. It is 'catching on to' this universal element that enlightens and extends the child's imagination. To the dullest adolescent these basic elements of life are as real and as moving as to intelligent ones. It is upon this recognition of common feelings that improvement in the use of English will depend.

As a subject, the rest of English disappears and the true function of language is put to its proper use: thought, communication. In the process of discussing problems and putting forward suggestions they learn to arrange their ideas logically. In discovering information they practise their reading and learning to select relevant data. The progress is steady, sometimes rapid, because the drive behind their work is the need to say or write what they think or have seen or have done personally. It is first hand reporting.

Similarly there is no History, Geography, Science, Needlework, Art, Craft and Music as such. All are involved to a greater or lesser degree in the matter under discussion and the ploys in action.

These 'centres of interest' are connected closely with the pupils' needs, and these, being in their fourth year are largely covered by the following considerations:

What is my town really like? How does it work?

What am I? How do other people see me?

What are other people like? What makes them act as they do?

How can I earn my living?

What am I going to do with my life? How can I make the most of it?

Put like this it sounds very ego-centric, but it is obvious that each one has so many ramifications . . . civic, psycholigical, historical, mathematical, geographical, architectural, financial — that no child can find itself enclosed in a separate world. Even looking at their town from the top of a high building and finding on the map what they are looking at is an entirely new experience in accuracy for all the members of the group. Seeing the model and maps of the town's future development with an architect to explain and answer questions extends their imagination as well as providing them with hard facts. Meeting the Mayor, Members of the Council, and the Town Clerk adds reality to civic organisation and provides opportunities for genuine expressions of opinion on both sides. (Could you tell us, please, why the housing list is always so long? .... £700 worth of damage is done to bus shelters every year by teen-age hooligans. What are you going to do about it?) Writing letters and giving votes of thanks introduce them to the formalities of social intercourse and help them to realise that these formalities carry them over the awkwardness of beginning and ending temporary associations. Formalities are not despised when the pupils discover them to be props and stays in a shifting social experience.

In all cases the individual pupils arrange their visits, doing the necessary letter writing, 'phone calls, welcoming and introducing, speeches of thanks and written acknowledgements. Two pupils will arrange one visit for a whole group, and at the beginning of term the visits are discussed and allocated, and as the replies come in a calendar is developed. In this part of the work they would include visits to sewage disposal units, water works, hospitals, clinics, nursery schools, parks department, the Town Hall, libraries, museums, art galleries. Some of these activities are shared, i.e. a small group go to each and report back to the rest. Those girls doing a course with a social bias would concentrate on this side while those doing a home-biased course would look at the town as a shopping centre and a housing area, surveying facilities and comparing bargains, as well as doing the basic organisation of town life.

'What am I, and how do other people see me?' may sound very self centred but what adult begins to understand others until he understands himself? Individual needs for knowledge of their own physiological processes, for admiration, for friendship, for hobbies, for money, for success are discussed using television broadcasts, films, film strips, books, magazines ('letters to the editor' are excellent stimuli), visiting beauty specialists and fashion shows.

'How can I earn my living?' is not only concerned with visiting factories, offices, large stores, hospitals, etc., to discover facts about wages, chances of promotion, working conditions, side benefits and the type of work involved, but is also concerned with what employees think of their work, what qualifications are necessary, how they are obtained, one's responsibility to one's work, to one's employer, to one's union. We have found that local employment exchange officials, bank managers, personnel managers of local firms, local magistrates, police officers, welfare officers are very willing to come to talk to the pupils and are very successful in stimulating thought. Any event of local interest which influences the social setting of our pupils is used to bring the wider implications into focus. Quarrels with coloured neighbours lead to trying to find out about their customs and attitudes. A group of char-women ganging up on a coloured bus conductor introduces and illustrates the concept of intolerance. Teenage crime reported in the papers is discussed, analysed, recorded in graphs, and letters on this subject occurring in the correspondence columns are weighed up. As well as the human problems involved, influence of the printed word is also judged in the light of their own reactions.

Once the pupils have become aware of the extent to which their everyday opinions are determined by prejudice — though they would not express it thus — it is possible to explore the world of advertisement. Here the B.B.C. help by producing excellent programmes on this subject, i.e. 'The World of Work' of May 1965 and the programme for technical school students. There are unending examples in our everyday life to illustrate and provide material for every type of enquiry ranging from 'Are the cut prices in self service stores real bargains?' to 'Should the moral standards of parents govern the behaviour of young people?' Nor are these mere debates with words as currency. The collection of evidence, the recognition of what constitutes evidence to support an argument, play a more important part than the argument itself. The attempt to get inside someone else's skin helps us all to live with each other.

Science is timetabled to ensure that laboratories and a specialist are available when needed. Their work is closely linked with the course and grows out of it. They all do human physiology in connection with their study of themselves and their study of sexual development. According to the bias of their course, they explore the advantages and disadvantages of detergents and other cleaning materials, the hardness and softness of water, the workings of electrical appliances in the home, the mysteries of plumbing, the hygiene of food preservation, town water supplies, sewage disposal, etc., and they learn to follow up their own interests independently on occasional 'projects' lasting half a term.

The Art, Craft and Needlework they do is all part of the course and may, or may not, be timetabled according to the staffing arrangements. Much of this side of the work deals with home decoration, and includes flower arranging, the study of wallpapers, furniture, dress design, pottery, screen printing, making their own outfits for their first job and making children's clothes and toys. The difference lies not so much in what is done, as in how it is done. Pupils move about the school and the town according to the needs of the individual work they are doing and one form may be scattered in a dozen different places. There may equally well be 40 or 50 pupils meeting in one place with tea and cakes (planned and prepared by a group of 3 or 4 girls) to look at an exhibition they have produced and to discuss it with each other and the staff. There is a tremendous amount of work in the original planning and in the final checking up and evaluation of each piece of work. There is the constant need to deal with individual calls for help and to cope amiably and tactfully with situations which one can see will lead to failure or excessive waste of time before success is reached. This is, perhaps, the most difficult part of the task for responsibility must not be removed from the pupil if it can possibly be avoided.

We have found that 20 to 25 pupils to one teacher for this part of the course is a reasonable ratio, and that best results are obtained if one teacher is responsible for most of that special course work, with an allocation of 4 or 5 sessions out of ten each week. Other members of staff work as sources of specialist information and skills. Domestic Science, Science, Literature, Drama, Music, Art and Mathematics are biased towards the needs of the central course and may spread into the time allocated to it. It is equally true that the central course may run into time allocated to other subjects, especially when visits are being arranged.

'All boys and girls need to develop, as well as skills, capacities for thought, judgement, enjoyment, curiosity. They need to develop a sense of responsibility for their work and towards other people and to begin to arrive at some code of normal and social behaviour which is self-imposed' (*Half Our Future*, para. 76, page 27, H.M.S.O. 1963).

This is, perhaps, the touchstone by which we judge the value of this course, and it has been necessary to evolve a method of testing at a practical level how far the pupils have developed 'some code of moral and social behaviour which is selfimposed'. We use 'initiative' tests to do this for we feel that a selfimposed code can only be judged by its practical application. At the beginning of the year pupils are given a day in which to prepare and complete a simple piece of discovery for which they have to look up information about routes, times of buses and trains, for a half day visit to some place of interest in the locality. Before, during, or after the visit they discover some supplementary information and after completing the visit write up the whole episode. This takes a total of three sessions during which each pair of students is responsible for every part of the arrangement. They discover the costs of the journey and collect the money from a member of staff together with the fee for a telephone call back to school from their destination. If any emergency demands further telephoning, money they spend on this is refunded if the extra call is justified. The students are given some task at their destination which involves talking to curators, attendants, police, etc. or buying pamphlets or cards which check on their arrival. Each pair, of course, goes to a different destination and on arrival, each member of the pair has work there which is different from that of her partner.

Except with very slow pupils, no correction of the plans is made at any stage by the teacher. If the pupils get on the wrong bus, read the wrong timetable, or lose their way, they have to use their own initiative to put things right. Each group has a set time to report back to school and variations from this have to be accounted for in detail. Two or three of these minor initiative tests are done in the first two terms, then in the third term they are given a week completely free of any timetabled work and three tasks to complete during the week.

(1) A day's visit to a distant spot of historic, geographical or artistic importance which involves preparing maps, discovering information, preparing picnic meals, and travel arrangements.

(2) A garment or piece of craft to complete. The craft includes pottery, basket work, cooking for a party or family, illustrating a child's story, decorating a room or alcove, arranging the publicity for a charity appeal, etc.

(3) A 'literacy test' which takes various forms. It can be a straight-forward criticism of one of the books presented, or a summary of reports such as those given in *Which?*, or a play reading which can be produced by a group of girls.

All pupils choose one task from each of these sections and they are then responsible for:

(a) arranging their own timetable and approaching the staff whose rooms they will have to use,

(b) allocating the time so that it is most effectively used. This is particularly necessary as they have to buy and prepare food for their picnic meals and any other cooking tasks they have chosen, and arrange their work so that the firing of pots, using machines, etc. does not lead to wasted time,

(c) completing their work and arranging it for exhibition and discussion at the final 'party',

(d) recording in diary, account and timetable from all they have done.

The staff running these courses check that timetables are possible, give advice when absolutely necessary, issue money against estimates (which have to be reasonable), check up on progress in the few cases which get bogged down, each member of staff concerned, having worked with this group for a whole year, knows when appeals for help are genuine and judges exactly how much to give without removing the pupil's responsibility for her work.

This week of work with complete responsibility for themselves weeds out the pupils very effectively. Fundamental inability to take responsibility shows up clearly. Ability to plan, persist, to cope with frustration, to adapt plans to reality, to be polite under all circumstances, are demonstrated every day. All members of staff have been amazed by the efficiency and ability to work unsupervised which the students — all average or below average in mentality — have shown.

Those completing the week's work satisfactorily are awarded a certificate listing the qualities they have shown during this week and during the year. To have proved that one can work efficiently without supervision, that one is reliable, conscientious and hard working and that one can rise to the occasion is a useful introduction to adult life.

These qualities, acknowledged as valuable in the social field, are equal in value and parallel in importance to the store of specialist knowledge, the ability to analyse the factors in a problem, the mental capacity to classify and eliminate. As imagination is the touch of genius in this field, so is sympathy in the social field. This side of education has been too long neglected for it satisfies the developing emotions of the adolescent more effectively than scholarship. I am convinced that this is the sphere we must explore in our secondary education for our children.

Epilogue

In the samples of work presented, and they are but samples, we have covered interesting and lively approaches to mathematics learning, both within the classroom walls and outside of them.

On page 43 will be noted a brief account of some team teaching. A monograph published by the Exeter Institute of Education (1) describes in greater detail another experiment in team teaching, involving both second and third year pupils. Since the conjoint teaching of Science and Mathematics was part of this experiment it provides also an example of the blurring of these subject boundaries.

In a recent publication *Mathematics Laboratories in Schools* (Bell 1968) prepared for the Mathematical Association will be found a description by D. J. Lumbard of Brislington School Bristol of the provisions for conjoint learning of Science and Mathematics by the younger pupils at that coeducational comprehensive school.

It is hoped that our offering will serve at least three useful purposes:

(a) Be of some support and encouragement to those beginning to change their approach.

(b) Remove some of the sense of isolation which at present exists among many like minded workers in the field.

(c) Cause some comparison to be made of the action of Part 2 with the thoughts of Part 1.

Bibliography

(1) *An Experiment in Team Teaching. Themes in Education No. 6* Exeter Institute of Education (May 1968).

(2) A book in the Education Today series:

Topical D. B. Boothman (Longmans) (1967) describes in detail the work of a team of teachers in a coeducational secondary school in an attempt to provide outgoing and relevant courses for their older pupils of average and below average ability.